LOGIC WORKBOOK FOR
GRITTY
KIDS

created by Dan Allbaugh   illustrated by Anil Yap

Table of Contents

Welcome my friend! I'm so glad you're here.
Are you ready to go? The start is so near.
In the pages to come you'll be put to the test.
Are you up for the challenge to give it your best?

Each section will test different things that you know.
Each section gets harder the further you go.
If you feel overwhelmed on a puzzle you start,
remember the start is the hardest of parts.

Don't be discouraged. Don't think to quit.
Use logic. Keep going. Show us your grit.
The answers are kept in the back of the book.
Stuck and need help? Then go have a look.

When you've finished them all, showed grit, and believed
a certificate shows just what you've achieved.

FIND THE HIDDEN MEEPLE

SOMEWHERE INSIDE!

Spatial Reasoning

It can be hard to try something new
not knowing if you will fail if you do,
but these are presents wrapped in a bow.
Every new thing is a great chance to grow.

On the pages beyond you'll do some cool stuff.
By the end you'll be saying, "That wasn't that tough."
In the section that follows there's so much to learn.
You'll be using your mind to rotate and turn.

Which shadow is correct?

Circle the same two pictures.

Connect the missing halves.

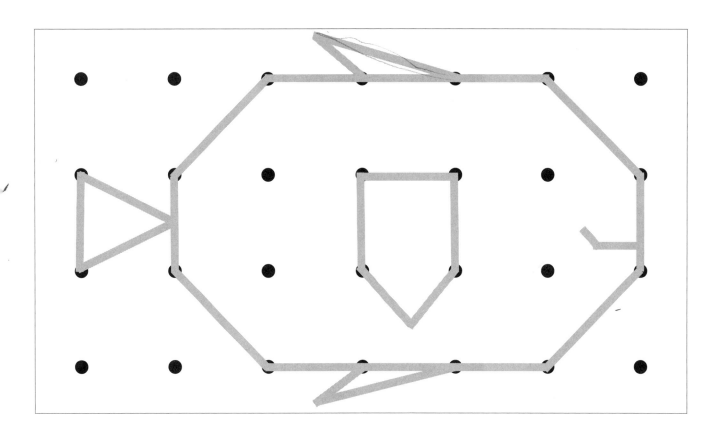

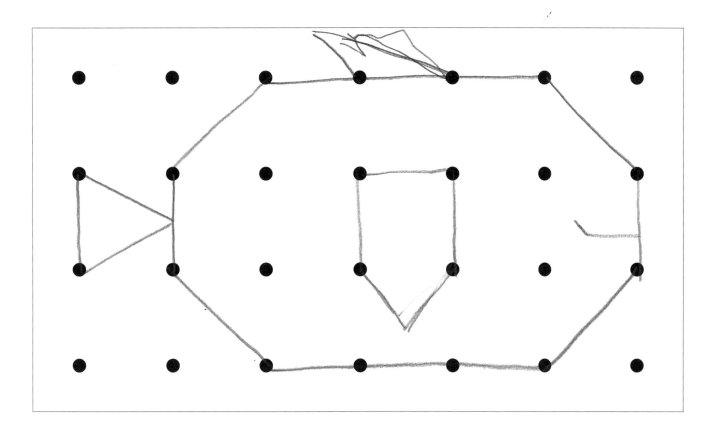

**Baby Bear has lost his mother.
Which path will get him back to her?**

E

D

C

B

A

Which path leads
back to Momma?

Match the missing part.

9

Match the side view with the top view. Write answers in the gray boxes.

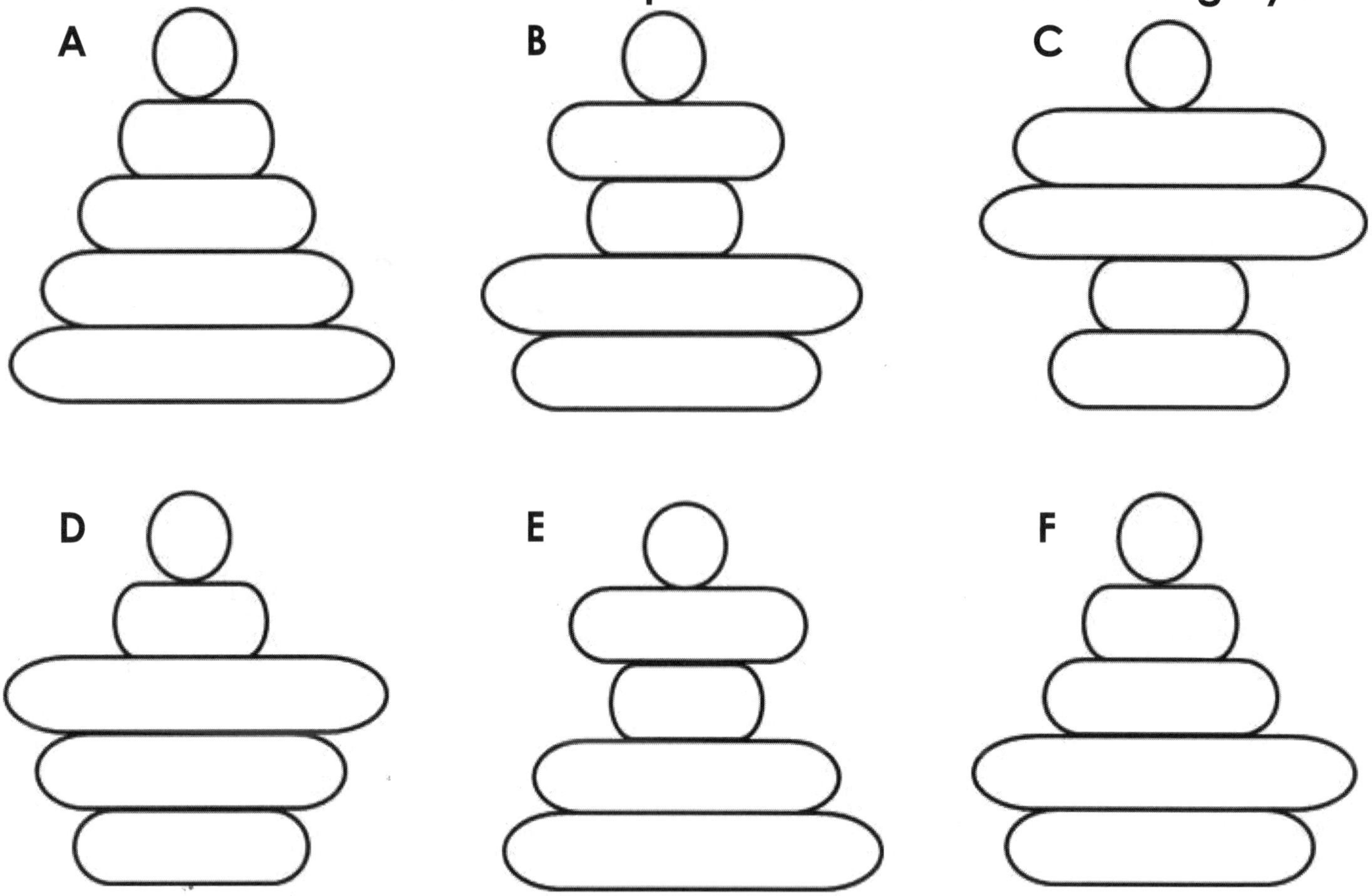

A

B

C

D

E

F

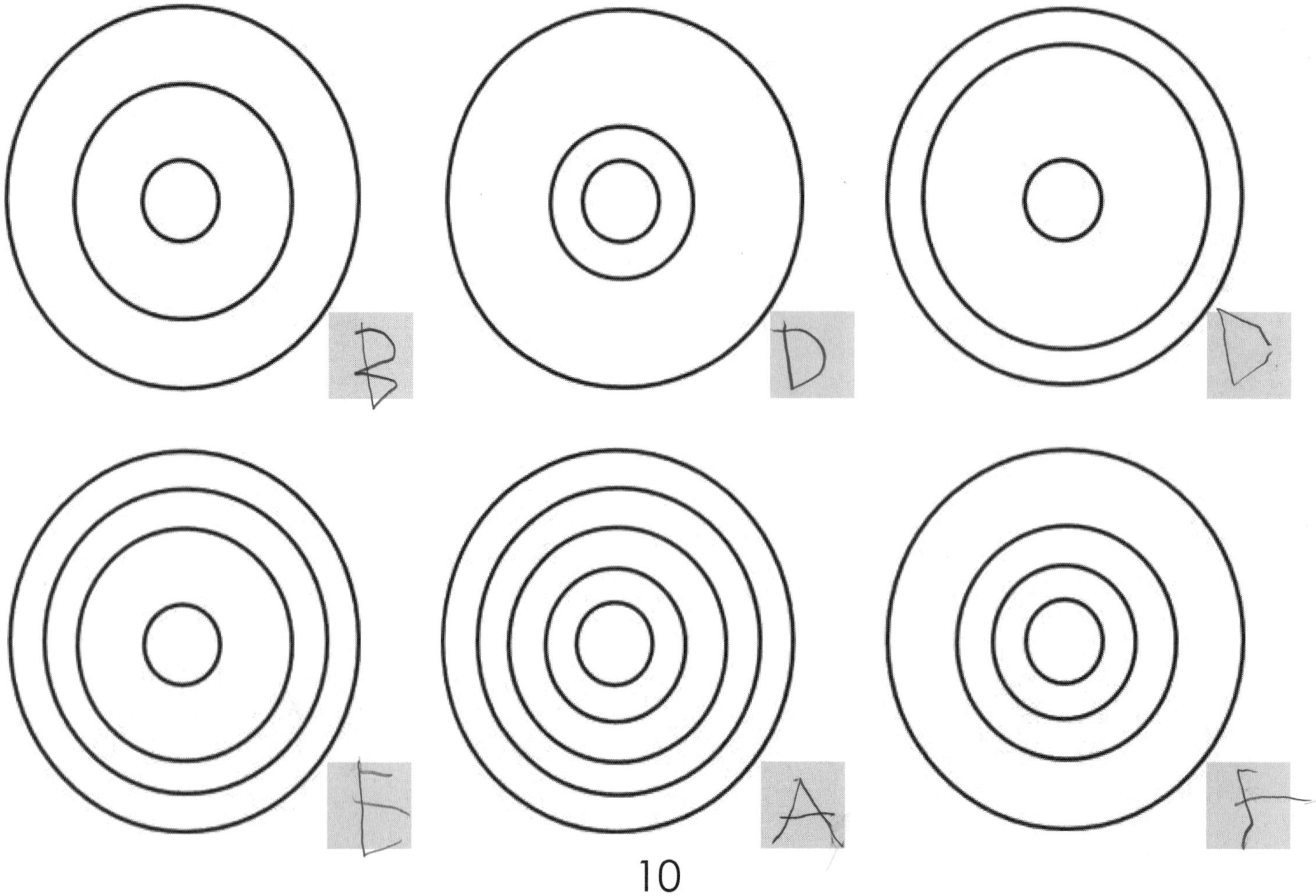

B

D

D

F

A

F

10

Match the figure on the left with the blocks used to make it on the right.

Each of these knots is different.
Count the number of ropes in each knot.

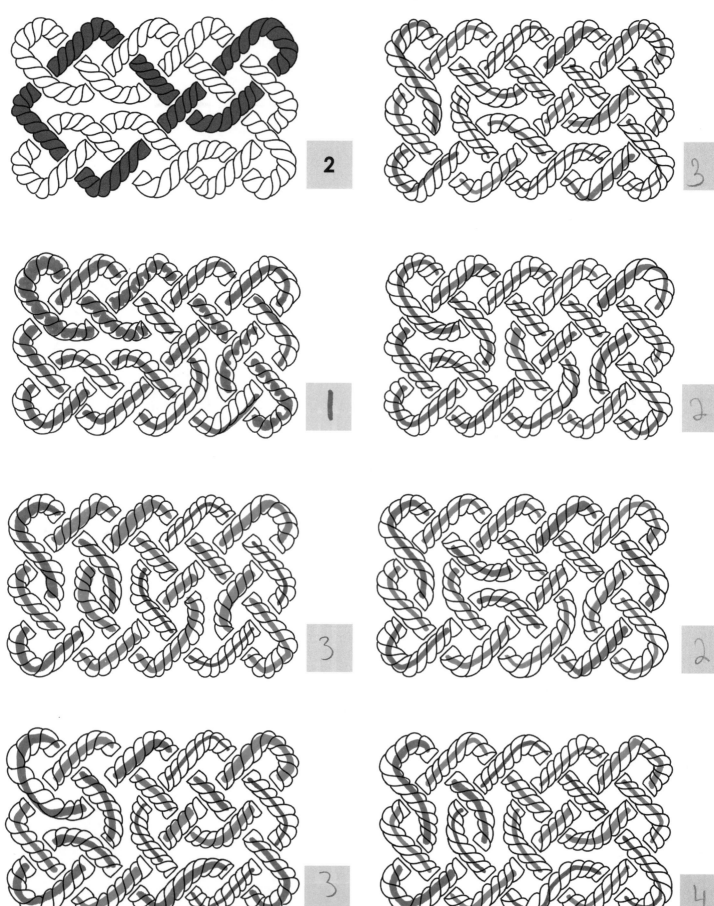

12

How many hay bales are there?

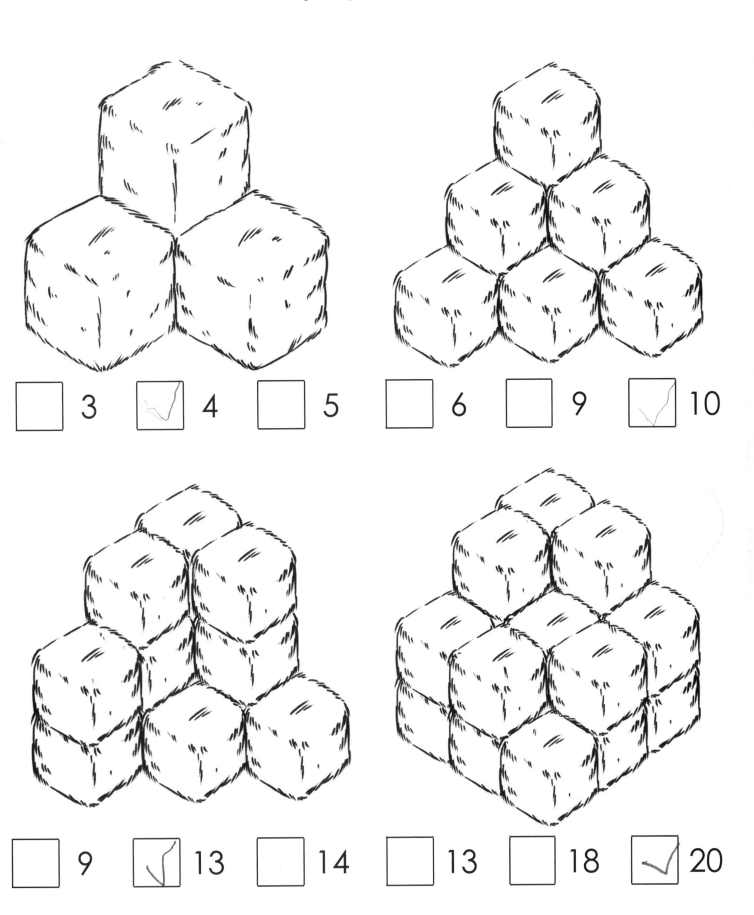

☐ 3   ☑ 4   ☐ 5   ☐ 6   ☐ 9   ☑ 10

☐ 9   ☑ 13   ☐ 14   ☐ 13   ☐ 18   ☑ 20

13

Which way will the gray gear spin? Circle the correct answer.

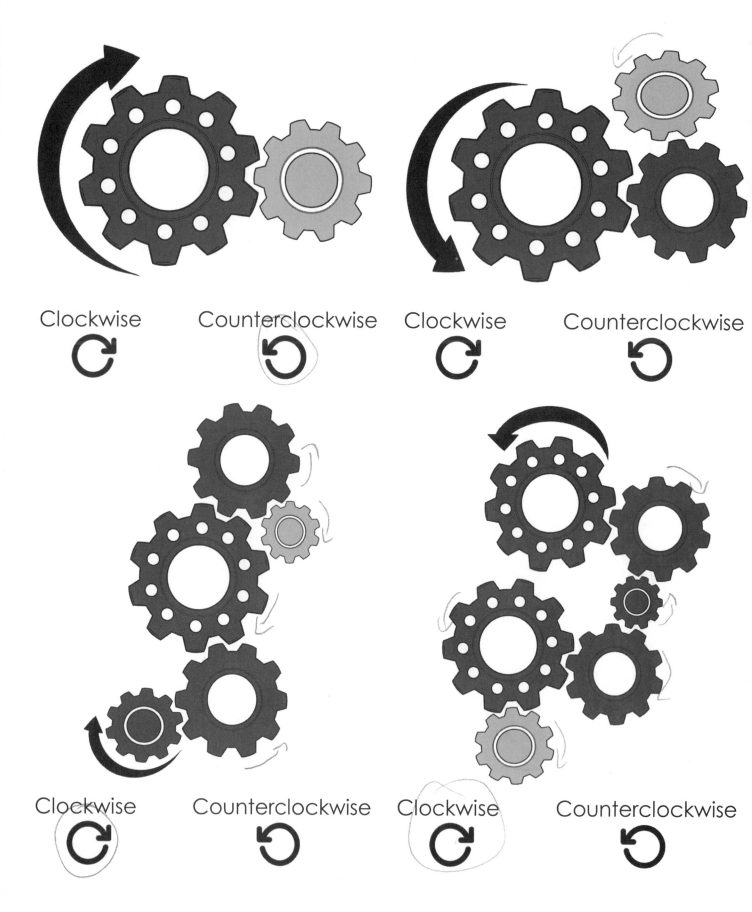

Clockwise

Counterclockwise

Clockwise

Counterclockwise

Clockwise

Counterclockwise

Clockwise

Counterclockwise

What shape in group 2 is the same shape as group 1?

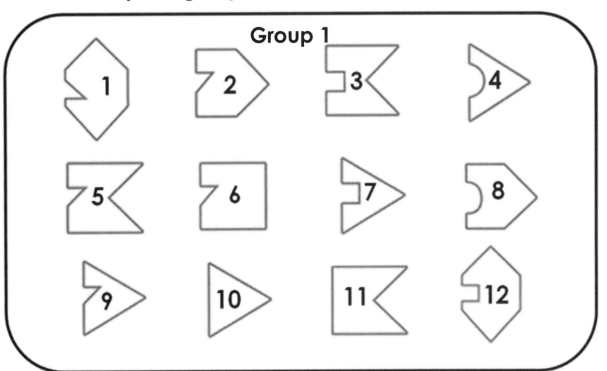

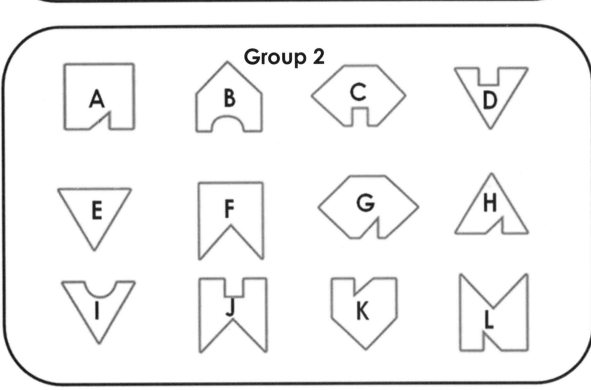

1 = [G]   5 = [ ]   9 = [ ]

2 = [ ]   6 = [ ]   10 = [ ]

3 = [ ]   7 = [ ]   11 = [ ]

4 = [ ]   8 = [ ]   12 = [ ]

15

Fun with lines!

Connect the matching numbers without crossing lines and staying inside the box.

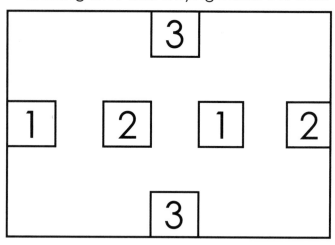

Can you figure out how to connect all nine dots with four straight lines without lifting your pencil or retracing?

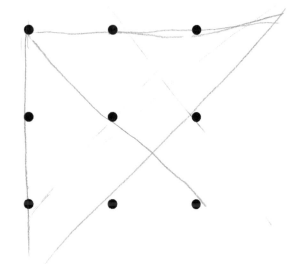

Begin wherever you want and draw one line through all the doors, but you cannot go through the same door twice.

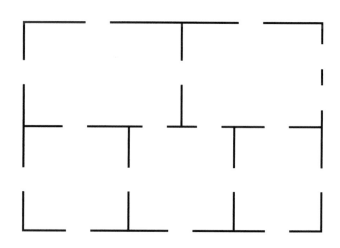

A farmer has 15 pigs to feed.
He starts in the lower right-hand stall represented by the circle.
Can you draw a path that allows him to visit each pig only once and exit through stall 1?

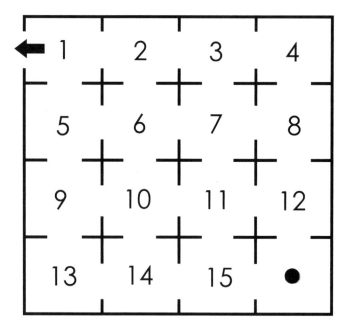

Begin and end at the black star.
Trace a path to make a continuous line that passes through all the dots without retracing.

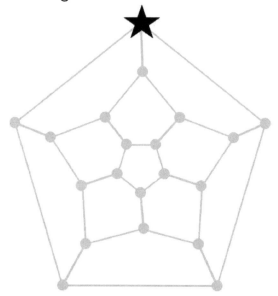

16

Math Puzzles

Add things up. Takeaway.
You use math skills every day.
Although these puzzles may be new,
you've got the talent within you.

Work through the games until they're done.
It all adds up to lots of fun.
Your never give up attitude
will bring success to all you do.

Lambie is on his way to school.
Can you trace the shortest path?

SCHOOL

18

Figure out the value of each shape and write the answers in the boxes provided.

What is Lambie's value? **6**

What is Dad's value? **4**

What is Mom's value? **3**

What is the barn's value? **5**

19

For each puzzle, place available numbers into empty squares so that the sum is equal to the number indicated.

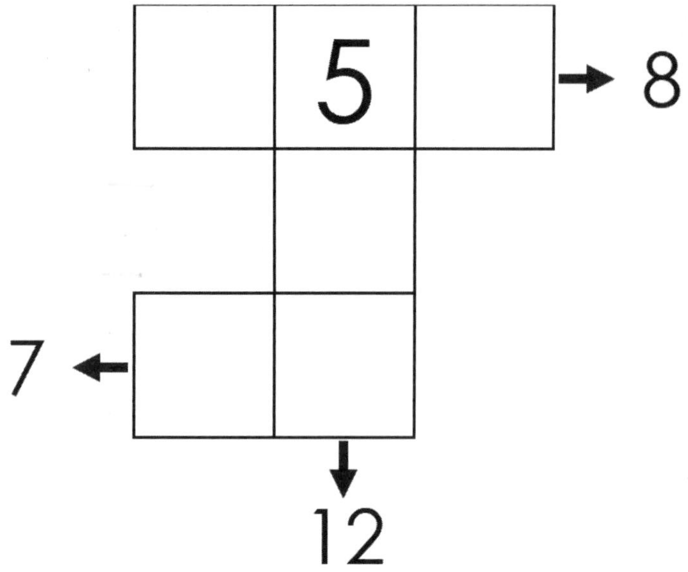

Puzzle 1

| | 5 | | → 8 |

→ 12 (down)
7 ← (left)

Available numbers

1 2 3 3 3
3 3 4 5 6

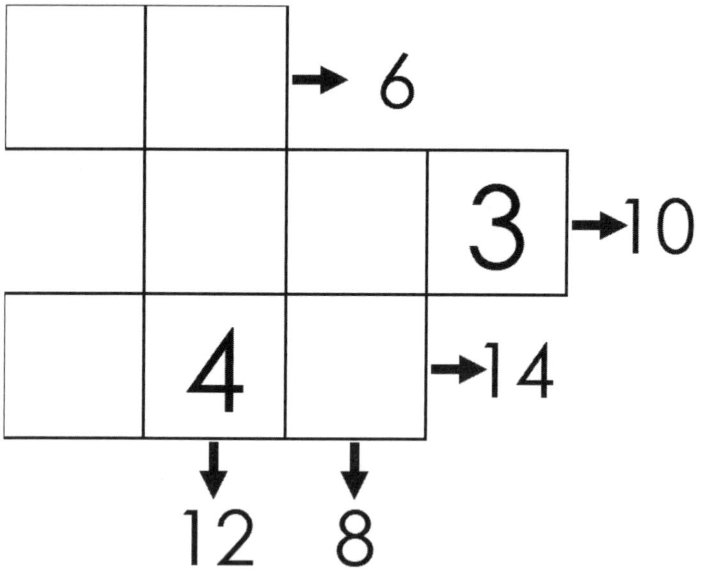

Puzzle 2

		→ 6
		3 → 10
4	→ 14

↓ 12   ↓ 8

Available numbers

1 2 2 3 3
4 5 5 6 6

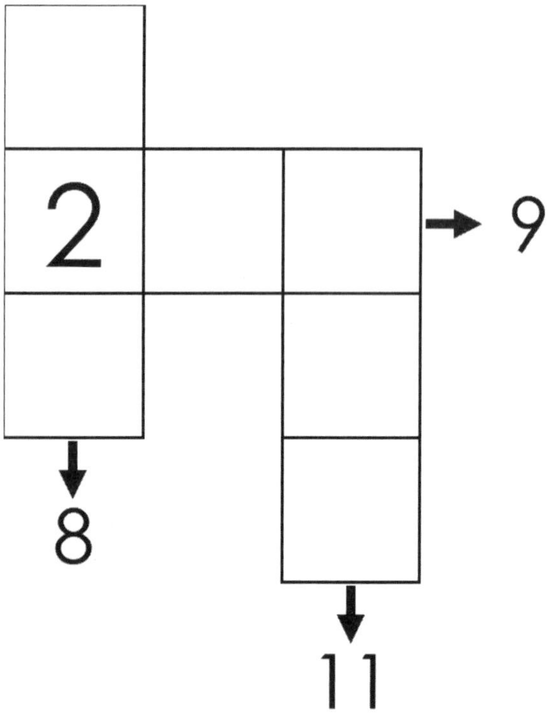

Puzzle 3

| 2 | | → 9 |

↓ 8
↓ 11

Available numbers

1 1 1 2 3
4 4 4 4 6

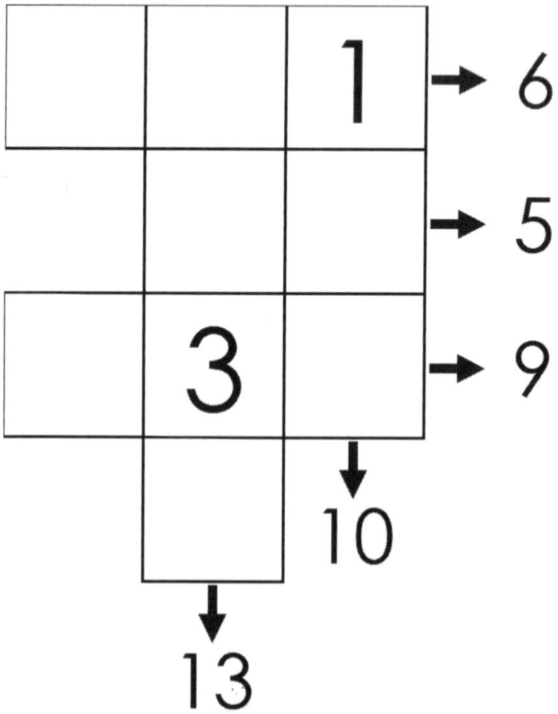

Puzzle 4

		1 → 6
		→ 5
	3	→ 9

↓ 13   10

Available numbers

1 1 2 2 2
3 3 4 5 6

20

Fill in the gray squares with the correct number to make each equation true.

$$5 + 4 = 9 \qquad 9 + 4 = 13$$

$$+ \qquad + \qquad -$$

$$5 \qquad 3 + 4 - 3 = 4$$

$$- \qquad = \qquad = \qquad +$$

$$3 \qquad 12 - 6 = 6 \qquad 7$$

$$= \qquad + \qquad =$$

$$4 + \_ + 3 - \_ + 5 = 11$$

$$+ \qquad - \qquad =$$

$$\_ \qquad 3 + 10 - \_ + 5 + 4 = \_$$

$$+ \qquad = \qquad - \qquad - \qquad +$$

$$1 \qquad 2 + \_ - 1 + \_ = \_ \qquad 3$$

$$= \qquad - \qquad + \qquad = \qquad + \qquad -$$

$$\_ - 5 = \_ \qquad - 1 + 4 = \_$$

$$+ \qquad = \qquad - \qquad + \qquad =$$

$$7 \qquad 3 \qquad - 2 - \_ = 2$$

$$= \qquad = \qquad =$$

$$\_ - \_ - 6 = 4 \qquad 14$$

21

Fill in the gray squares with the correct operator (+ or -) to make each equation true.

7 $-$ 3 = 4

2 $+$ 4 = 6

10 $+$ 5 = 15

12 $-$ 4 = 8

6 $+$ 3 $-$ 1 = 8

4 $+$ 2 □ 5 = 7

13 □ 7 □ 4 = 10

11 □ 4 □ 6 = 9

7 □ 3 □ 5 □ 4 = 9

9 □ 4 □ 6 □ 2 = 9

12 □ 4 □ 11 □ 8 = 11

15 □ 6 □ 9 □ 12 = 6

4 □ 2 □ 1 □ 3 □ 5 = 5

8 □ 2 □ 5 □ 4 □ 3 = 2

11 □ 9 □ 13 □ 5 □ 6 = 4

8 □ 10 □ 4 □ 7 □ 18 = 11

5 □ 2 = 7

9 □ 6 = 3

18 □ 12 = 6

13 □ 5 = 18

9 □ 6 □ 2 = 5

5 □ 4 □ 3 = 6

15 □ 5 □ 8 = 12

8 □ 7 □ 11 = 4

8 □ 2 □ 3 □ 1 = 4

1 □ 5 □ 2 □ 4 = 4

16 □ 12 □ 9 □ 2 = 17

13 □ 4 □ 12 □ 11 = 16

7 □ 3 □ 2 □ 1 □ 4 = 1

8 □ 5 □ 9 □ 4 □ 1 = 9

13 □ 9 □ 5 □ 7 □ 8 = 2

9 □ 12 □ 5 □ 14 □ 6 = 18

22

Divide each grid into rectangular or square pieces.
Each piece must contain exactly one number.
That number must represent the area of the rectangle.
The first one is completed as an example.

The sum of each row (↔) and column (↕) are given.
What number does each animal represent?

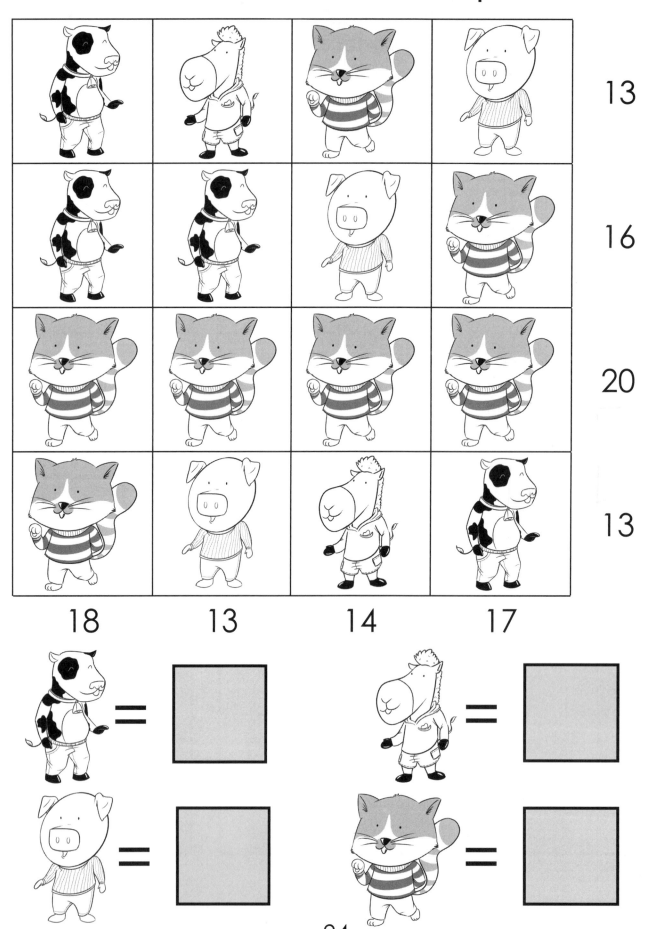

Each puzzle must contain all numbers 1 to 9.
Some numbers have been provided.
Fill in the gray boxes to make the equations true.

Puzzle 1

3	+	▨	+	6	17
+	■	−	■	−	
▨	−	5	+	▨	8
−	■	+	■	+	
1	+	▨	−	2	6
11		10		4	

Puzzle 2

9	+	▨	+	▨	18
−	■	−	■	+	
▨	−	3	−	▨	2
+	■	−	■	+	
6	+	▨	−	5	5
8		1		8	

Puzzle 3

6	−	▨	−	4	−7
+	■	−	■	+	
▨	+	7	+	▨	11
−	■	+	■	+	
▨	+	▨	−	▨	−1
4		4		13	

Puzzle 4

2	+	▨	−	▨	1
+	■	+	■	+	
▨	−	1	−	3	4
−	■	+	■	+	
▨	+	▨	−	▨	0
5		11		19	

Puzzle 5

▨	+	3	−	▨	8
+	■	+	■	+	
▨	+	5	−	8	−1
−	■	−	■	+	
▨	−	▨	+	▨	12
5		7		19	

Puzzle 6

2	+	▨	−	▨	8
−	■	+	■	−	
▨	+	7	−	▨	8
+	■	+	■	−	
8	−	▨	−	▨	1
5		22		−2	

5	11	17	23	29	35
		28	34		
21					51
		20		32	
12	18				
37			55	61	
1		13			31
					71

4	1	6	3	8	5
		14	19		
			26	31	
7			6		
	37		39		
	10				
					34
				25	

7	8	10	13	17	22
			26		
		30			42
		27		34	
3		6			
		23			
35			41		
	15				29

2	4	3	6	5	10
12		23			
				21	
	26				
	16		30		
10					74
		7			
			18	17	

Within every large square, each row (↔), column (↕), and mini-grid must contain the numbers 1, 2, 3, and 4.

Puzzle 1 (top left):

	3	4	
4			2
1			3
	2	1	

Puzzle 2 (top right):

	3		4
2		1	3
4			1

Puzzle 3 (middle left):

	1		
3		2	
	2		3
		1	

Puzzle 4 (middle right):

4	2		
2			
		3	2

Puzzle 5 (bottom left):

3		1	
	1		4

Puzzle 6 (bottom right):

		2	1
3	2		

27

The mouse is hungry for cheese but can only carry three pieces!
For each puzzle, find the highest possible total value of cheese.
Start anywhere and collect three numbers by following the paths.
No jumping or going back over a path twice.

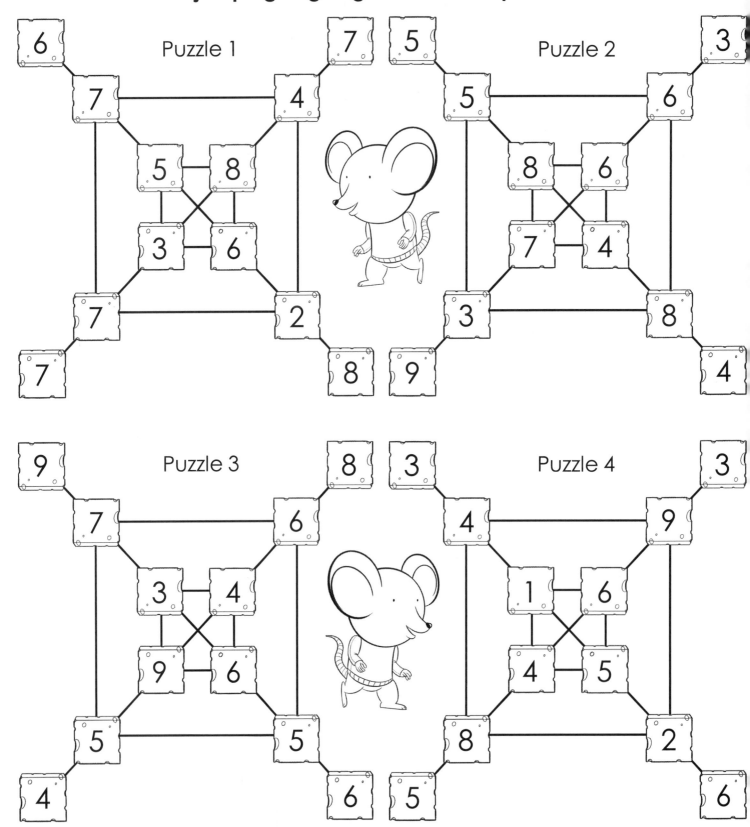

Puzzle 1

Puzzle 2

Puzzle 3

Puzzle 4

Which animal pairing will balance the teeter totter?
Circle the correct answer.

A   B   C   D

Determine the pattern for each shape and write the correct answer in the gray area.

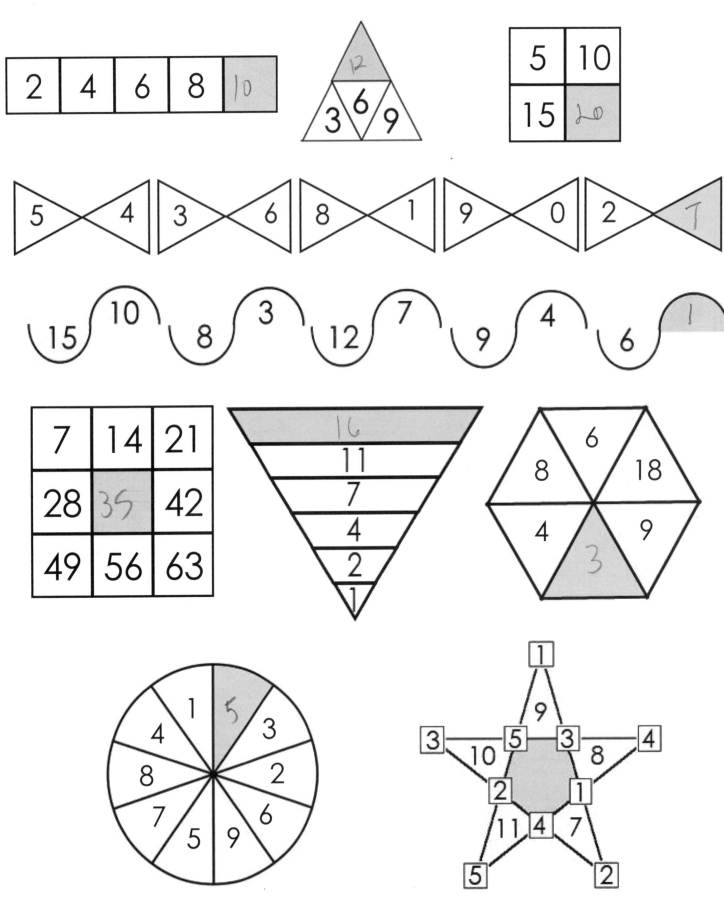

Logic Problems

Don't stop now, you've got the heart.
It may be hard, but you are smart.
You're doing great! You've achieved!
Great things occur when you believe.

Consider order step by step
to figure out what happens next.
That's called logic. Work it out.
That's what this is all about.

Circle who will win the race if everybody starts at the same time, stays in their own lane, and goes the same speed.

What is the correct picture for each relationship?

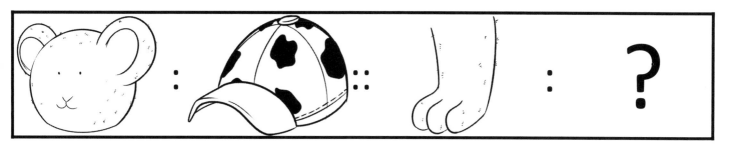

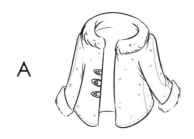 A    B   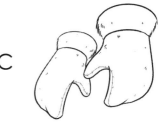 C

 A    B   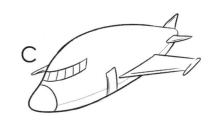 C

   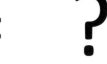

  A    B    C

What date is Lambie's birthday?

- Lambie's first day of school is one week after swim lessons ended.
- Lambie's birthday is three days before his basketball game.
- Swim lessons ended 13 days ago from today.
- Lambie's trip to Grandma's is the Saturday before his first day of school.
- Today is the 25th.
- Lambie's basketball game is two weeks after his trip to Grandma's.

Can you use this calendar to help figure out Lambie's birthday?

Sunday	Monday	Tuesday	Wednesday	Thursday	Friday	Saturday
1	2	3	4	5	6	7
8	9	10	11	12	13	14
15	16	17	18	19	20	21
22	23	24	25	26	27	28
29	30	31				

FIRST DA

GRANDMA'S HOUSE

34

Where is everyone standing?

- Skunk is four spots to the left (←) of Squirrel.
- Dad is between Squirrel and Mom.
- Cow is six spaces away from Dad.
- Squirrel is two spots to the right (→) of Horse.
- Mom is five spaces to the right (→) of Lambie.
- Horse is in spot 4.
- Cat is three spaces to the left (←) of Mom.
- Lambie is in between Skunk and Horse.

Can you draw lines from each character to where they are standing?

Where is everyone seated at the game table?

- Horse is seated six seats clockwise (↻) from Mom.
- Lambie is two seats clockwise (↻) from Dad.
- Badger is seated two seats clockwise (↻) from Pig.
- Raccoon is seated between Lambie and Dad.
- Cow is across the table from Badger.
- Mom is seated three seats counterclockwise (↺) from Raccoon.
- Dad is seated three seats counterclockwise (↺) from Cow.

Can you draw a line from the character to where they are sitting?

How did everybody finish the game and what were the scores?

- Horse finished with three points more than Pig.
- Badger finished with half as many points as Dad.
- Lambie had four times as many points as Mom.
- Raccoon finished three points ahead of Cow.
- Pig finished with two points.
- Mom lost to Raccoon by nine points.
- Cow had twice as many points as Horse.
- Dad finished four points behind Lambie.

Can you fill out these squares to show what place everybody finished and what their scores were?

	Points	Place		Points	Place

37

Put numbers in each puzzle so that no two consecutive numbers are connected by a line.
For one of these, this is not possible. Can you figure out which one?

Use numbers 1-7

Use numbers 1-8

Use numbers 1-9

Use numbers 1-9

Use numbers 1-9

Use numbers 1-9

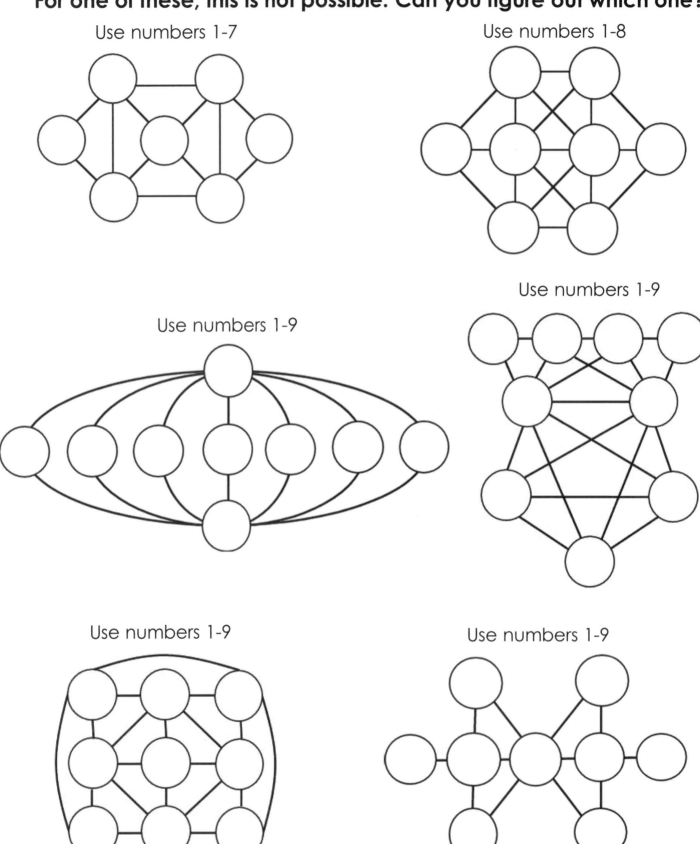

38

Connect the matching shapes without overlapping any lines or shapes.

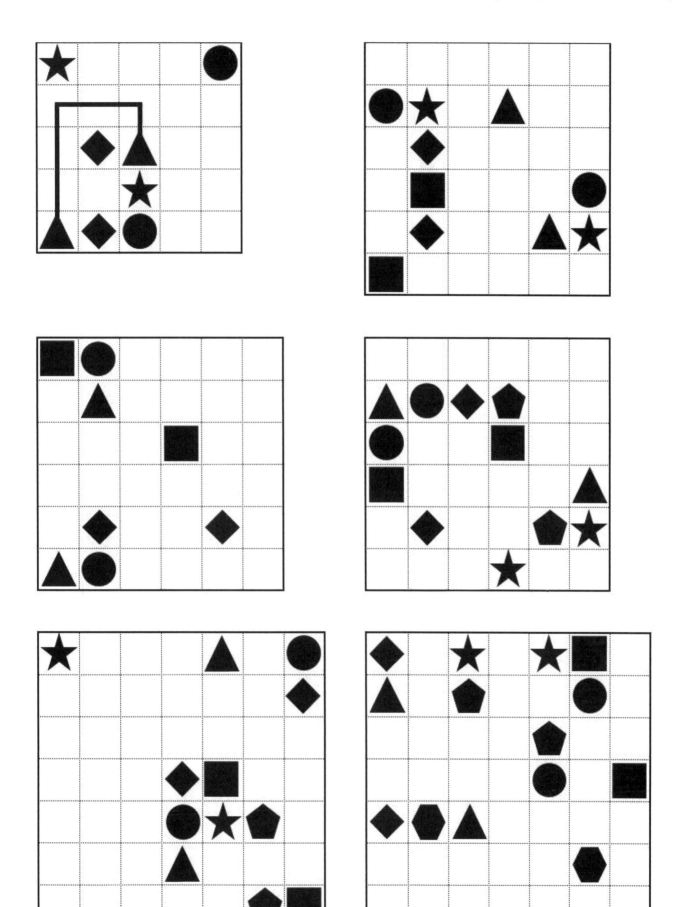

What is the correct path Lambie should take to get home without stepping in a puddle?

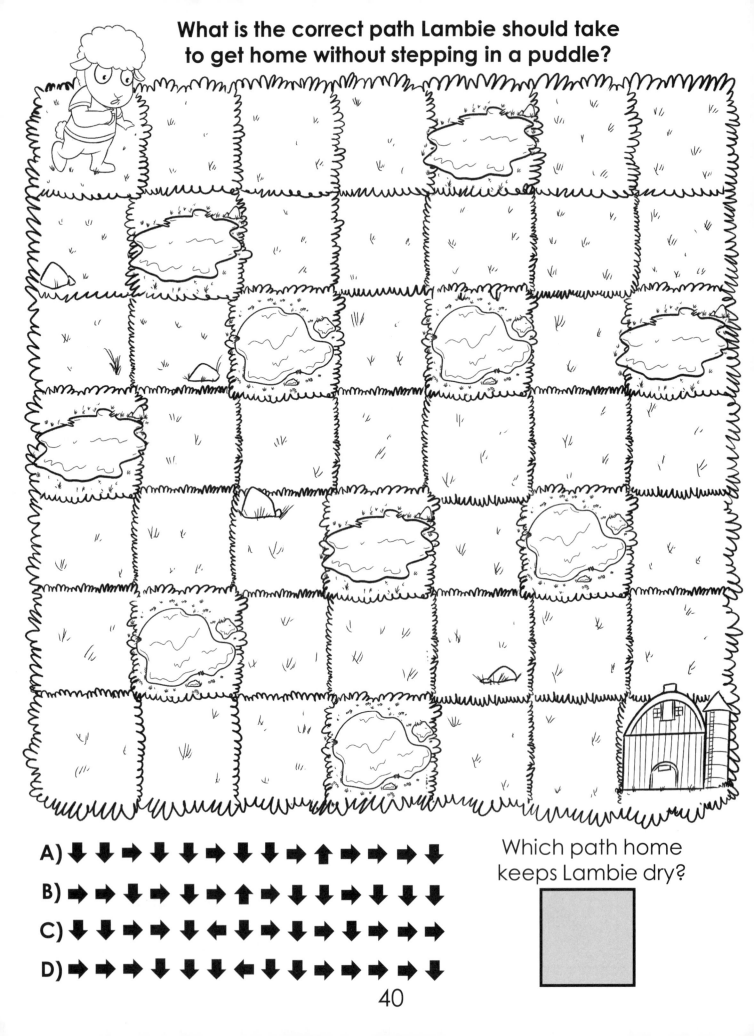

Which path home keeps Lambie dry?

A) ⬇⬇➡⬇⬇➡⬇⬇➡⬆➡➡➡⬇

B) ➡➡⬇⬇⬇⬆➡⬇⬇➡⬇⬇⬇

C) ⬇⬇➡➡⬇⬅⬇➡⬇⬇⬇➡➡➡

D) ➡➡➡⬇⬇⬇⬅⬇⬇➡➡➡⬇

40

When Toad lands on a shape, he hops the represented three steps.

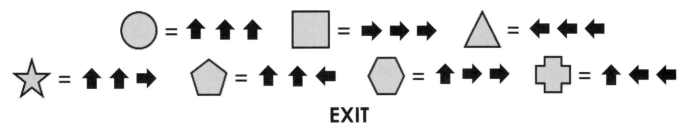

EXIT

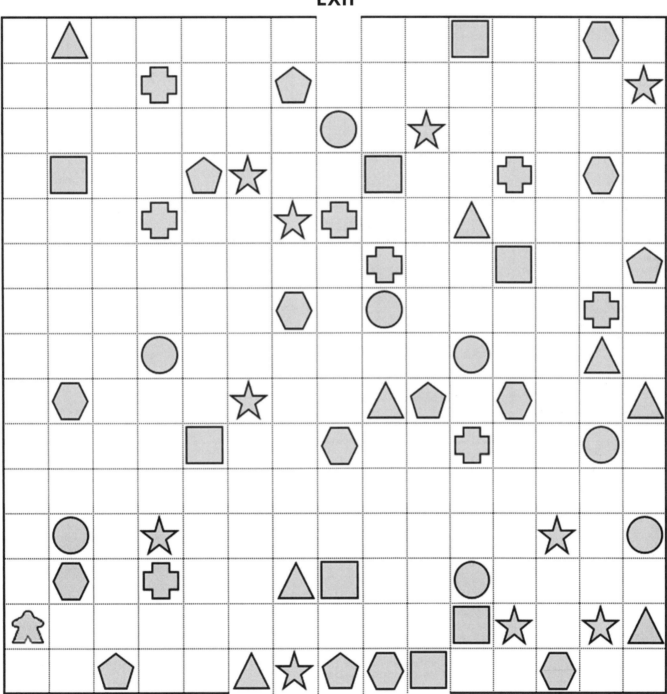

A B C D E

Which path leads
Toad to the exit?

41

It is lunchtime at school. The animals all have seating preferences.

- Kangaroo wants to share a corner with Lambie.
- Ostrich wants three seats between him and Turtle.
- Chameleon wants to sit on a side with two other animals.
- Beaver wants to be on the opposite side of the table from Lambie.
- Goat does not want to sit next to Kangaroo.
- Turtle wants to share a corner with Lambie.
- Koala wants exactly one seat between her and Ostrich.

Can you put each animal in a seat while meeting all their preferences?

Can you solve these brainteasers?
The answer may not be so obvious.

If Lambie were running a race and passed the person in second place, what place would Lambie be in now?

Hannah's mother has four children.
Three are named Nana, Nene, and Nini.
What is the name of the fourth child?

If Donkey is the 10th fastest and slowest runner in her school, how many students are there?

If tomorrow I said,
"The day before yesterday was Saturday",
which day is it today?

Mama Duck has seven daughters.
Each daughter has one brother.
How many ducklings does Mama Duck have?

If it takes one monkey one minute to eat one banana, how long will it take five monkeys to eat five bananas?

Every day the number of lily pads in a lake doubles.
In eight days, the entire lake is covered by lily pads.
How many days does it take to cover half the lake?

Draw a single non-intersecting loop that passes through all circles. When you reach a circle, the line must turn. The first one is started.

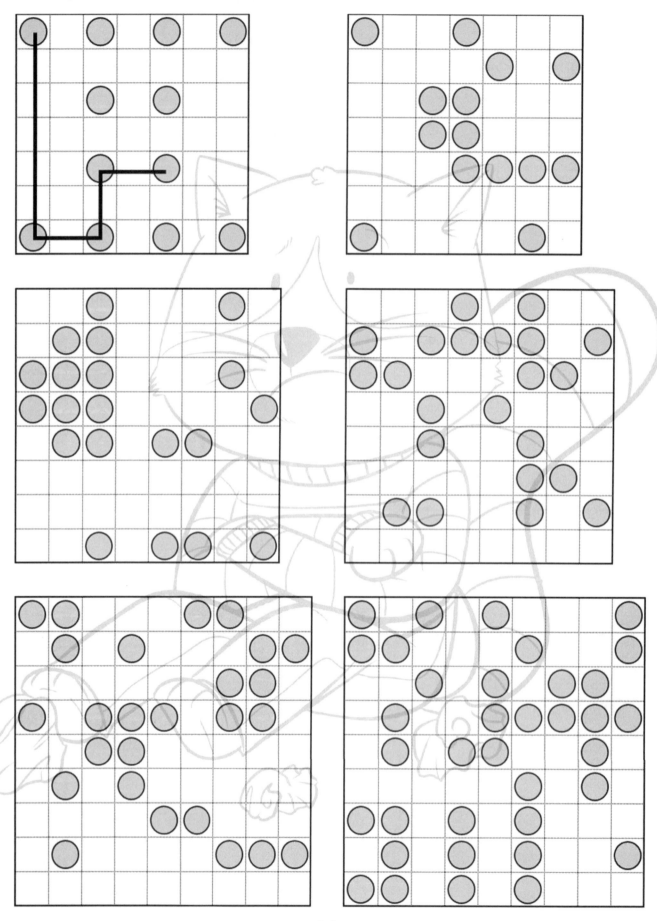

Word Games

Stop and think how far you've come.
You're doing great! You've overcome.
Let's shift targets. Let's change gears.
Words will be our focus here.

You've read them here. You know them well.
The words you use to speak and spell.
But now you'll use them differently.
Turn the pages and you'll see.

Circle the letter that cannot be made with the shapes on the left.

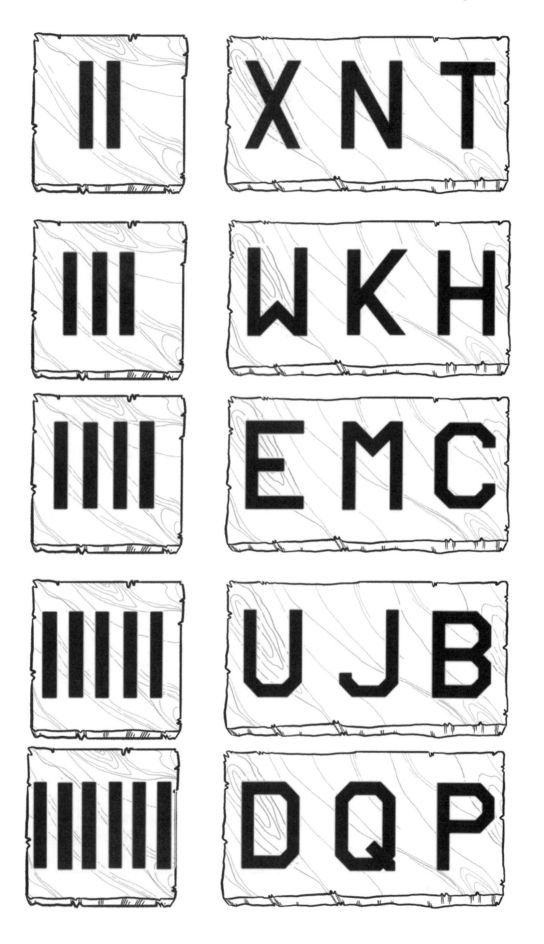

Use lines to connect the boxes and unscramble the word.

R C N O

A L B M

S L O I

R A N B

E F L I D

R W O G

O R A T C T R

A R R F M E

47

Cross out the extra letter in each animal's name.

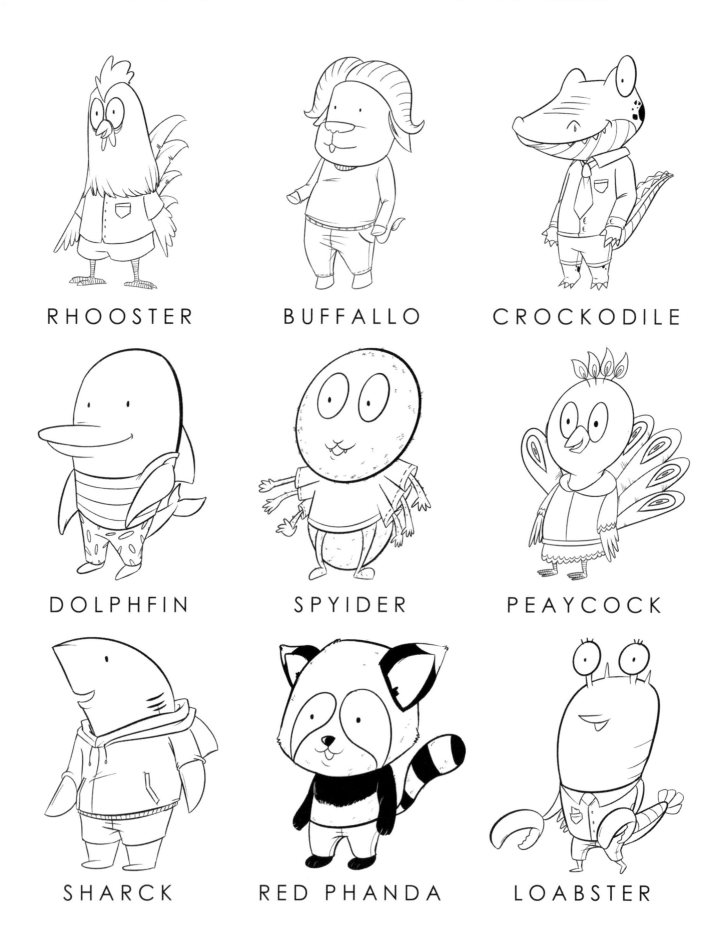

RHOOSTER

BUFFALLO

CROCKODILE

DOLPHFIN

SPYIDER

PEAYCOCK

SHARCK

RED PHANDA

LOABSTER

Find the hidden words.
Words can go in these directions: ➡ ⬅ ⬆ ⬇ ⬊ ⬋ ⬈

```
M R A F G F B B W G Z A F J J
V L G O I Q O A R R U X A D I
O O O L A M B I E P P B T A Q
C O W C K J T B A M C A T Q U
S H N W O T N J X D R E I I R
F A K H Y B C E A Y P W T P U
P R A C T I C E P A K D U E G
D H S N F T I T I Y R Y D B B
H G D U L B E F G V F L E H C
E O Q O U J U Y Y I Q Y S S H
Q Z R E K B R Y B D N E B T J
I W G S K A C N D T M D D M A
C D E T E R M I N A T I O N Q
M M F D P N R P G W M C O U A
W F D P E R S E V E R A N C E
```

ATTITUDE	COW	GAMES	LAMBIE	PRACTICE
BARN	DETERMINATION	GRITTY	PERSEVERANCE	SHEEP
CAT	FARM	HORSE	PIG	YET

49

Write the names of the animals in the correct space.

In the story below there are hidden animal names in some of the words. Can you find all of them?

~ANIMALS~

ape	bat	bee	boa	cat	doe	eel	fly
hare	hen	lion	mole	~~moth~~	owl	ram	rat

A B C D E F G H I J K L M N O P Q R S T U V W X Y Z
15 3 8 22 12 26 6 20 16 10 19 4 24 13 9 1 23 7 21 2 11 17 14 25 5 18

Message 1

I CANT GIVE UP ON ME
16 · 8 15 13 2 · 6 16 17 12 · 11 1 · 9 13 · 24 12

ID NEVER KNOW HOW GREAT ID BE
16 22 · 13 12 17 12 7 · 19 13 9 14 · 20 9 14 · 6 7 12 15 2 · 16 22 · 3 12

Message 2

WITH ANY PASSION YOU PURSUE
14 16 2 20 · 15 13 5 · 1 15 21 21 16 9 13 · 5 9 11 · 1 11 7 21 11 12

YOUR SUCCESS IS UP TO YOU
5 9 11 7 · 21 11 8 8 12 21 21 · 16 21 · 11 1 · 2 9 · 5 9 11

WHATEVER YOU MAY WANT TO BE
14 20 15 2 12 17 12 7 · 5 9 11 · 24 15 5 · 14 15 13 2 · 2 9 · 3 12

DONT QUIT
22 9 13 2 · 23 11 16 2

AND YOULL ACHIEVE YOUR DREAMS
15 13 22 · 5 9 11 4 4 · 15 8 20 16 12 17 12 · 5 9 11 7 · 22 7 12 15 24 21

Message 3

IT ALL HAPPENS BIT BY BIT
16 2 · 15 4 4 · 20 15 1 1 12 13 21 · 3 16 2 · 3 5 · 3 16 2

BUT YOU NEVER GET THERE IF YOU QUIT
3 11 2 · 5 9 11 · 13 12 17 12 7 · 6 12 2 · 2 20 12 7 12 · 16 26 · 5 9 11 · 23 11 16 2

SO WHEN YOU SAY I CANT DO IT
21 9 · 14 20 12 13 · 5 9 11 · 21 15 5 · 16 · 8 15 13 2 · 22 9 · 16 2

DONT FORGET
22 9 13 2 · 26 9 7 6 12 2

TO ADD A YET
2 9 · 15 22 22 · 15 · 5 12 2

Each of these foods has a double letter in the name. Can you fill in the blanks?

P E __ __ E R S

A __ __ L E

C __ __ K I E

M U __ __ I N

C A __ __ O T

B E __ __ I E S

W A __ __ L E

B U __ __ E R

C A __ __ A G E

S P A G H E __ __ I

P I __ __ A

B R O __ __ O L I

C H __ __ S E

E __ __ S

L E __ __ U C E

P I N E A __ __ L E

C H E __ __ Y

J E __ __ Y

Unscramble the words to discover the animal names.
The first one is done for you.

❶ DICE COLOR

CROCODILE

❷ NO RICH ROSE

_____

❸ JAB AT BRICK

_____

❹ SCOOT UP

_____

```
~ANIMALS~

GIRAFFE
HIPPOPOTAMUS
RHINOCEROS
JACK RABBIT
PRAIRIE DOG
CROCODILE
CENTIPEDE
OCTOPUS
MOUNTAIN LION
ELEPHANT
```

❺ FIG FEAR

_____

❻ PATIO PUSH MOP

_____

❽ IN A MOON UNTIL

_____

❼ NEAT HELP

_____

❾ RADIO GRIPE

_____

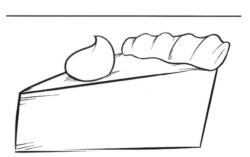

❿ DECENT PIE

_____

To make a word, take a letter or combination of letters from each barn.
Make four words for each group of barns.
The first word in each group has been done for you.

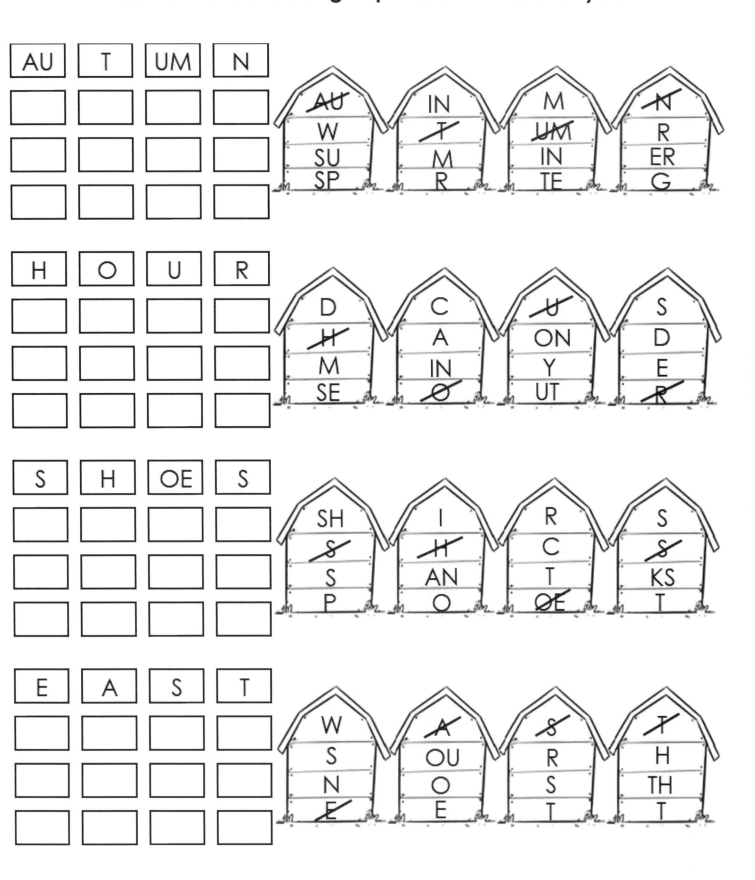

AU	T	UM	N

H	O	U	R

S	H	OE	S

E	A	S	T

Using the letters available, can you write down at least five words of any length for each puzzle? Use each letter at most only one time per word.

Follow the instructions to crack the coded message.

Coded message:

LITTL ELAMB IELOV EDTOP LAYIF HEHAD HISWA YHEDP LAYAL LDAYB
UILDI NGTOW ERSPL AYGRO UNDSL IDESJ UMPIN GHANG INGWA
GONRI DESBL OWING BUBBL ESCLI MBING TREES NEARL YALLA CTIVI
TIESW HENAS KEDHI SFAVO RITEH EEXCL AIMST HERES NOTHI NGILO
VEMOR ETHAN GAMES

Decoded message:

Print out the complete coded message in capital letters, with no spaces between letters. Mark a slash (/) between words as they appear to you.

···
···
···
···
···
···
···

Cleartext message:

Write out the complete message in plain English.

Can you figure out the phrase for each of these word puzzles?
Consider how the words are written, the number of times, their direction, and placement.

1 **R** **ROAD** **A** **D**	2 **CHAIR**	3 **MAN** / **BOARD**
4 **FOUR FOUR FOUR FOUR FOUR**	5 **CYCLE** **CYCLE** **CYCLE**	6 **HEAT**
7 **GO MERRY**	8 **READ**	9 **S S** **I I** **D D** **E E**

1	2	3
Crossroads		
4	5	6
7	8	9

Activities

How do you get to the top of the stairs?
One step at a time and soon you'll get there.
Your journey began when you took your first step.
You're well on your way but not done quite yet.

You've made it so far. You're nearing the end.
You are tough and determined. Your grit doesn't bend.
Activities follow on pages beyond.
You've got this. Keep at it. Keep moving on.

What was last month and what is next month?

LAST MONTH	THIS MONTH	NEXT MONTH
	MAY	
	SEPTEMBER	
	FEBRUARY	
	JULY	
	APRIL	
	OCTOBER	
	DECEMBER	
	JANUARY	
	JUNE	
	NOVEMBER	
	MARCH	
	AUGUST	

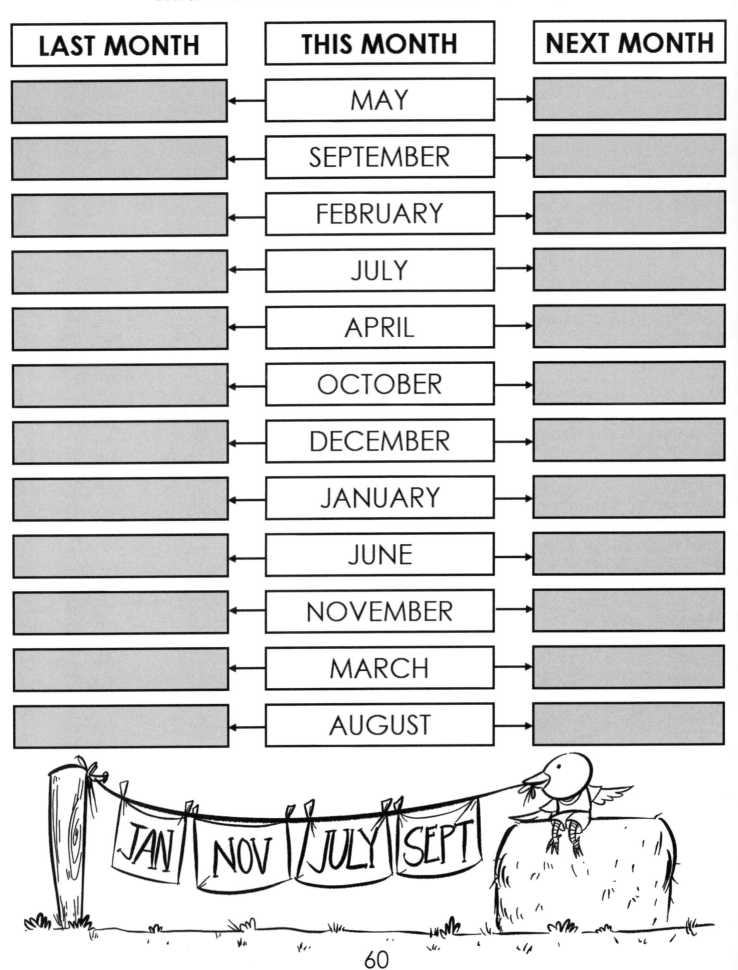

JAN   NOV   JULY   SEPT

What day was yesterday and what day is tomorrow?

YESTERDAY	TODAY	TOMORROW
	FRIDAY	
	WEDNESDAY	
	SUNDAY	
	THURSDAY	
	SATURDAY	
	TUESDAY	
	MONDAY	

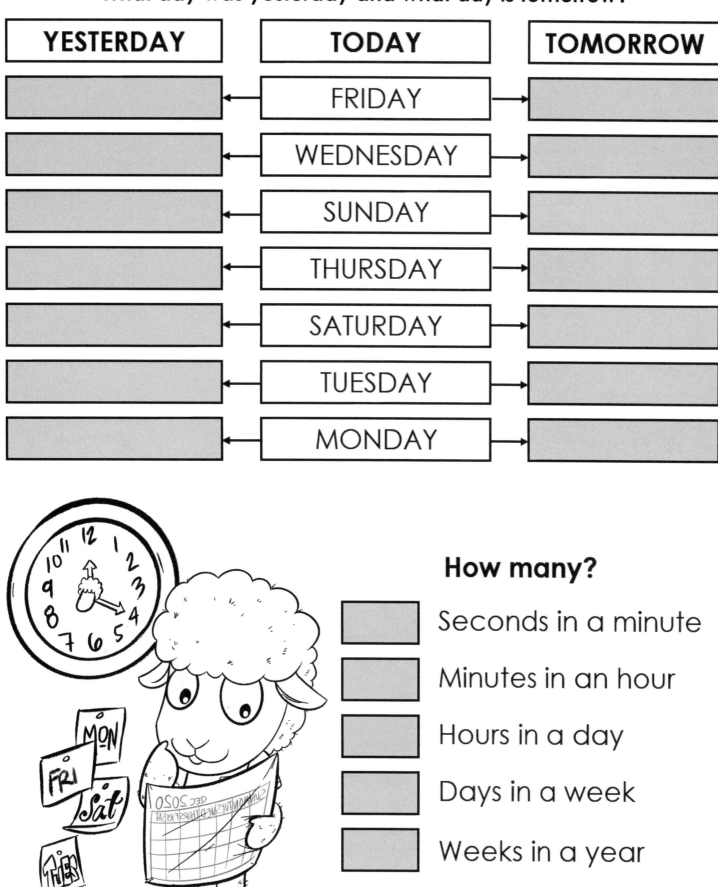

How many?

Seconds in a minute

Minutes in an hour

Hours in a day

Days in a week

Weeks in a year

Connect the dots!

Help Lambie get to his ball!

Hidden pictures!

Can you find?

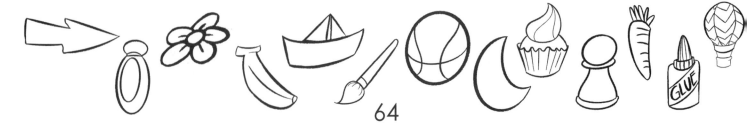

64

Can you find and circle 16 differences between these pictures?

Count the objects hidden in the drawing.

How many of each shape are there?

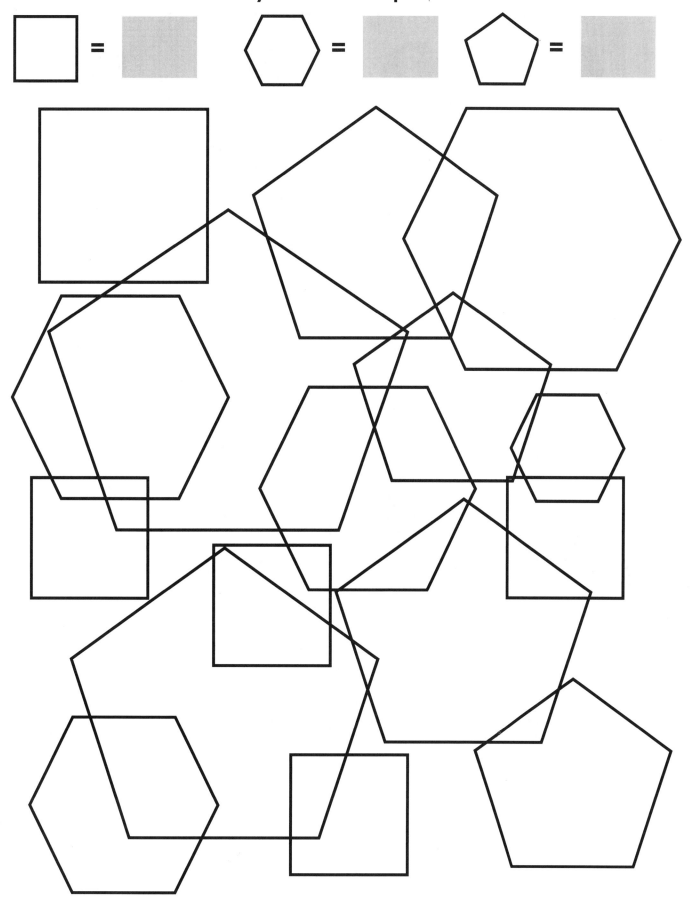

Animals in each row (↔) and column (↕) have something in common. What is it?

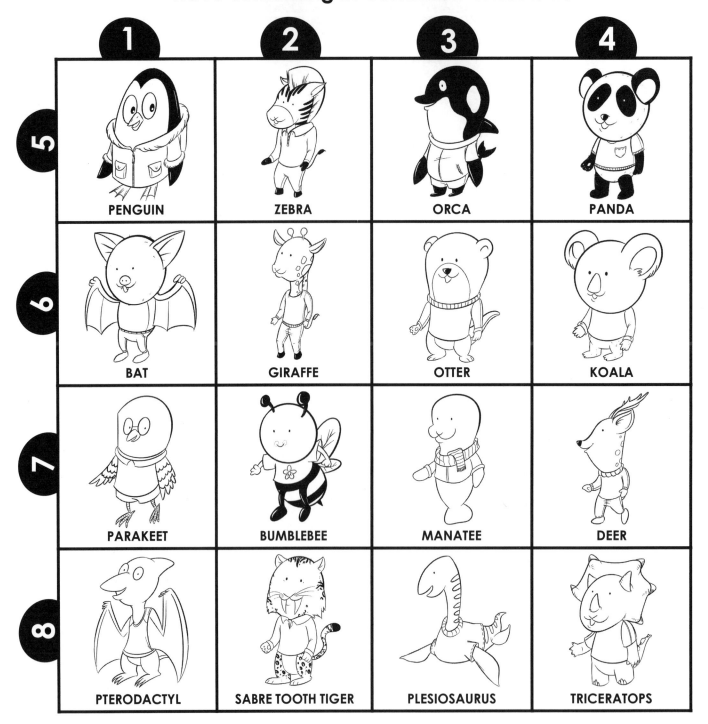

	1	**2**	**3**	**4**
5	PENGUIN	ZEBRA	ORCA	PANDA
6	BAT	GIRAFFE	OTTER	KOALA
7	PARAKEET	BUMBLEBEE	MANATEE	DEER
8	PTERODACTYL	SABRE TOOTH TIGER	PLESIOSAURUS	TRICERATOPS

They all...

____ A. can swim.

____ B. are extinct.

____ C. have a pattern.

____ D. are black and white.

____ E. have wings.

____ F. have "ee" in their names.

____ G. are mammals.

____ H. eat plants.

68

Complete each grid so that there are not four X's or four O's next to each other either horizontally (↔), vertically (↕), or diagonally (⊠).

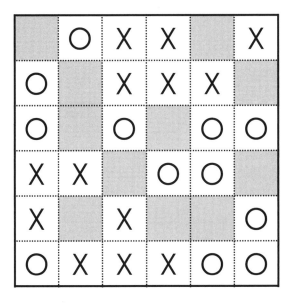

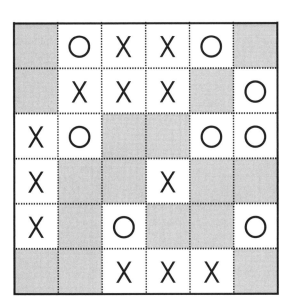

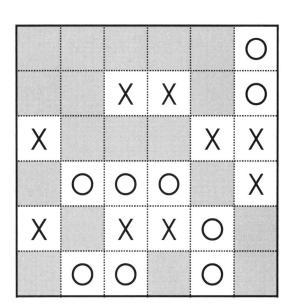

Fill in each grid with numbers 1 to 36 to make a connected path. You can connect numbers horizontally (↔) and vertically (↕). You must connect all 36.

Grid 1

	13			8	
15	16			9	6
		18	1		
		27	36		
22	25			34	33
	24			31	

Grid 2

15		17	18		20
	13			36	
7					22
6					23
	2			27	
4		30	29		25

Grid 3

	3	2	1	34	
5					36
12					31
13					30
18					29
	20	21	22	27	

Grid 4

		36	23		
	10			25	
	9			26	
		13	20		

Grid 5

	6			29	
8	1			32	27
13	12			23	22
	15			20	

Grid 6

4					31
		10	11		
		9	12		
17					36

Sometimes two words have similar meanings.
Can you match up words that mean the same thing?

fun	start
game	middle
fast	cap
jungle	hard
hat	leap
say	glad
house	create
right	contest
big	good
yell	forest
pretty	scream
excellent	smart
happy	home
begin	correct
tired	large
intelligent	sleepy
center	quick
difficult	beautiful
jump	enjoyable
make	tell

Draw Lambie!

Step 1

Step 2

Step 3

Step 4

Step 5

Step 6

Step 7

Step 8

Your turn!

Two-Player Games

You finished the puzzles. You challenged your brain.
Now games with another are all that remain.
Grab a parent or friend before you've adjourned.
Put to use all the tools and logic you've learned.

But remember to play with a smile on your face.
If you happen to lose, then do so with grace.
We all want to win. That's why we play.
Sometimes you'll lose and that is ok.

Save the Sheep!

GOAL

Fence in the most sheep by game end.

RULES

1. Each turn draw a line to connect two horizontal (↔) or vertical (↕) adjacent dots.
2. Making the fourth line of a box fences in a sheep, earning you a point. When you fence in a sheep you must move again.
3. Lines are drawn until all sheep are safe and fenced in. The player with the most fenced in sheep wins!

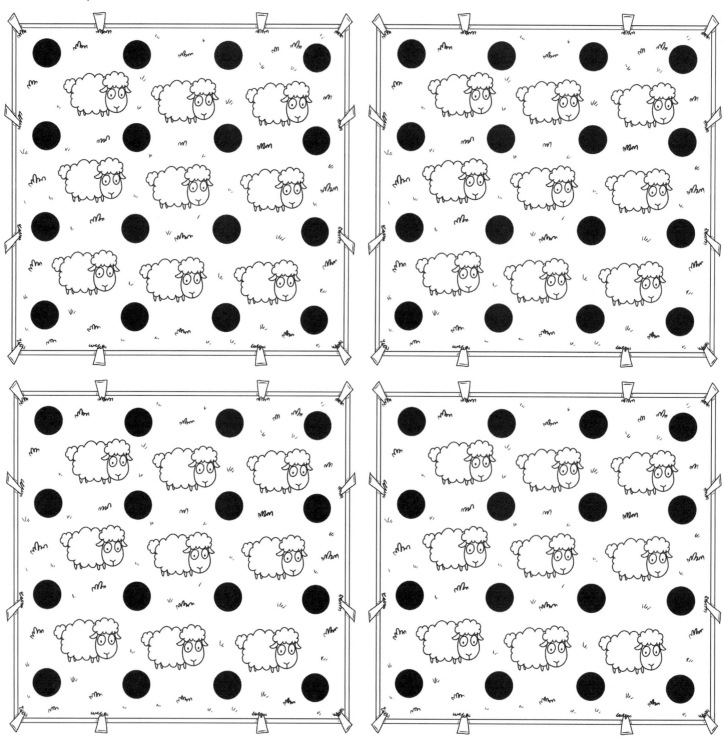

Ultimate Tic-Tac-Toe

GOAL
Win three games of tic-tac-toe in a row on the smaller boards to win on the larger board.

RULES

1. There is one large tic-tac-toe global board where each grid contains a small local board.
2. One player plays as X while the other player plays as O.
3. X goes first and can place their mark on any of the 81 spots on a local board.
4. X's placement directs O to where their mark may be placed. O must play in the corresponding grid of the global board by looking at the local board where X played. For example, if X played in the bottom right of a local board, then O must choose an open spot on the bottom right global board.
5. Play continues in this manner with players taking turns and sending their opponents.
6. Getting three in a row on one of the local boards wins that area and is marked as a victory on the global board with the winning symbol.
7. Once a local board is won by a player or it is filled completely, no more moves may be played there. If a player is sent to that board, then that player may place anywhere.
8. The winner is the person who can get three in a row on the global board.

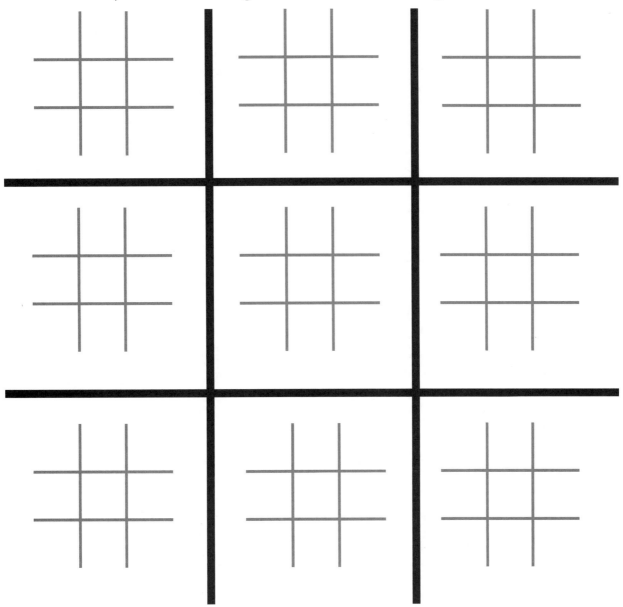

Blackout

GOAL
Force your opponent to fill in the last circle.

RULES
1. Take turns filling in as many circles in a row (↔) as you'd like. You must fill in at least one circle and can fill in up to the entire row.
2. The player who forces their opponent to fill in the last remaining circle is the winner.

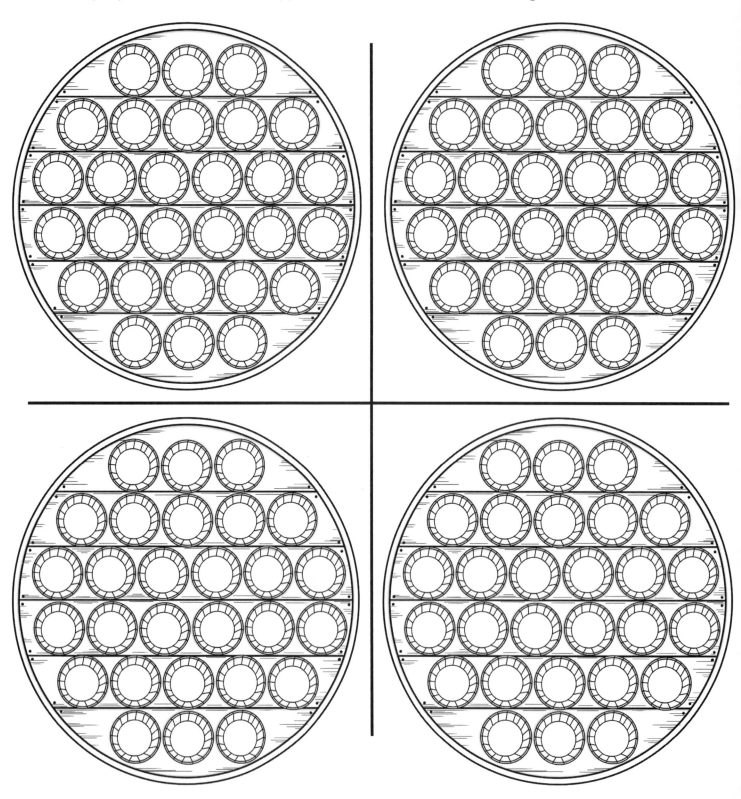

Crosscram

GOAL
Force your opponent to be unable to move.

RULES
1. Players take turn linking adjacent pairs of dots on the grid.
2. One player can only make vertical links (↕) while the other player can only make horizontal links (↔).
3. No dot can be linked more than once.
4. The first player unable to move loses.

Bridgit

GOAL

Form a continuous link across the board.

RULES

1. Players each own a symbol, either (•) or (◆), then take turns linking any two of their own adjacent matching symbols.
2. No two links may cross.
3. The first player to form a continuous link across the board from top to bottom (•) or left to right (◆), wins.

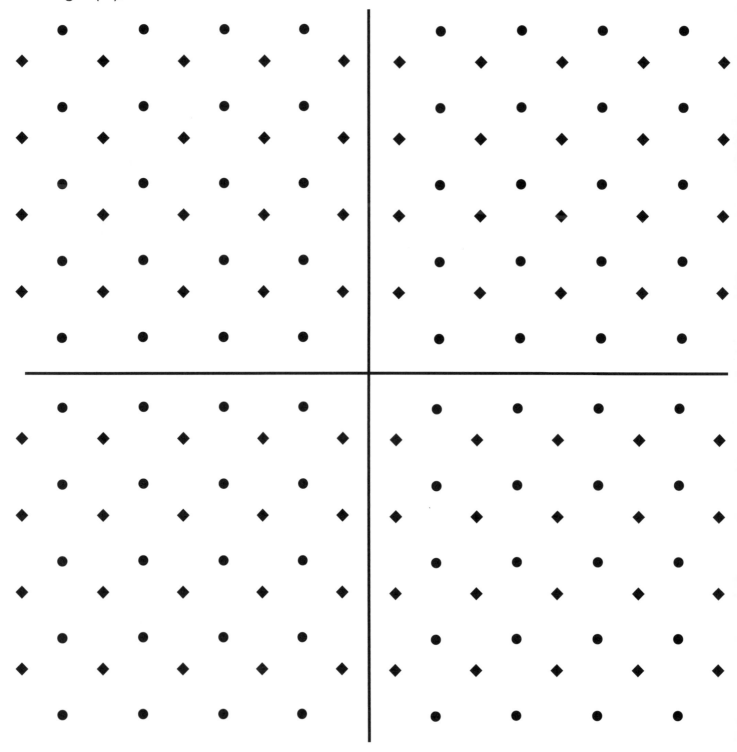

Order and Chaos

GOAL
One player tries to get five in a row; the other tries to prevent this.

RULES
1. Players take turns. On each turn either player can write an 'X' or 'O' in any open square.
2. The object of the first player (Order) is to complete a line of five 'X's or five 'O's in any direction.
3. The object of the other player (Chaos) is to prevent this.
4. Order wins as soon as a line of five is completed in any direction. Chaos wins if they prevent Order from achieving their goal.

Hex

GOAL
Create a chain across the board in your color (corners count as both).

RULES
1. Players take turns. One player draws solid dots. The other player draws open dots. Dots can be placed anywhere.
2. The winner is the first player to form a connected path linking opposite sides of the board with their dots.

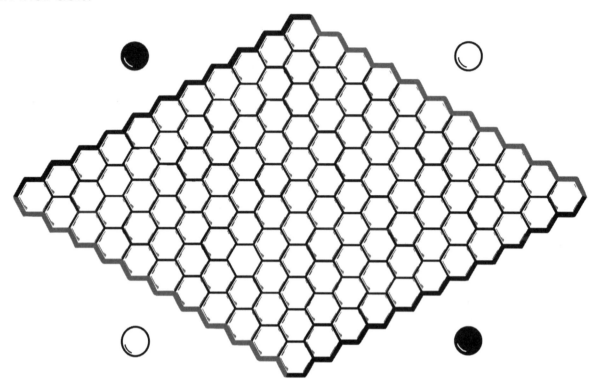

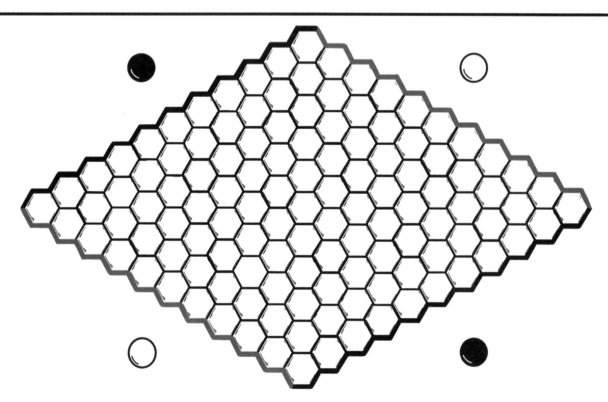

Snort

GOAL
Force your opponent to be unable to make a legal move.
RULES

1. Players each have a unique color.
2. Take turns coloring in a region with a restriction that two regions sharing a border cannot be the same color.
3. The first player unable to color loses.

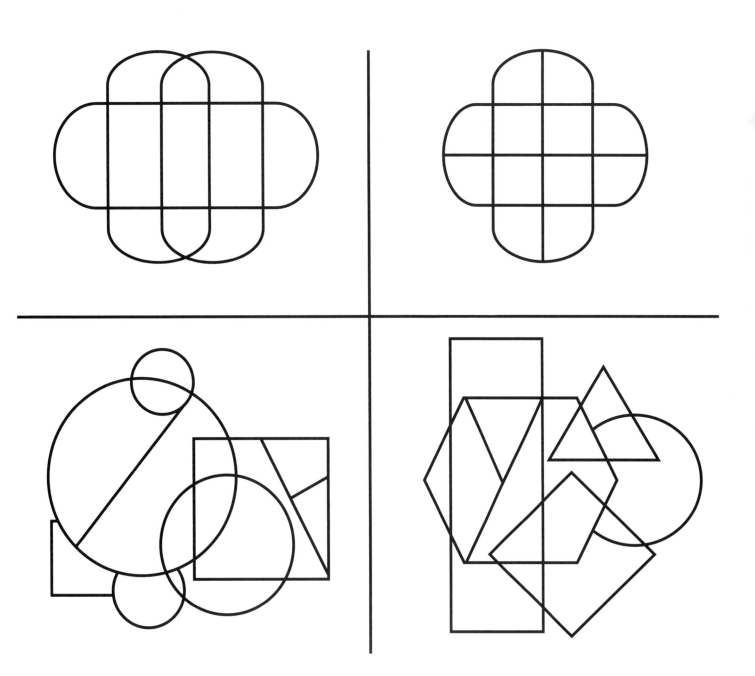

Sour Grapes

GOAL
Have the highest sum on grapes remaining after some spoil.
RULES
1. Players each have a unique color.
2. Take turns writing '1' in a grape of your choice using your unique colors.
3. After that take turns writing '2', '3', '4', and so on, in order (no skipping ahead).
4. After each player has written '10' there will be one blank grape. This is the sour grape.
5. The sour grape spoils all neighboring grapes. Fill in the sour grape and all neighboring spoiled grapes. Whoever has the highest sum of remaining numbers is the winner.

Sprouts

GOAL
Be the last player to draw a line without intersecting any other line.

RULES
1. Players take turns. On your turn, draw a line that either connects two sprouts or loop a line back onto a single sprout with the following restrictions:
   i) The line may be straight or curved, but it must not touch itself or any other line.
   ii) No sprout may have more than three lines connecting to it.

   Finish your turn by adding a new sprout somewhere on the line you just drew.
2. When one player is stuck and unable to move, the other player wins.

Sim

GOAL
Avoid being the first person to draw a triangle in your own color.

RULES

1. Players each have a unique color.
2. Players take turns tracing a single gray line between dots, each using their own color.
3. The first player who forces their opponent to complete a triangle with all three sides of their own color wins.
4. A triangle must be formed with dots at each point (interior triangles don't count).

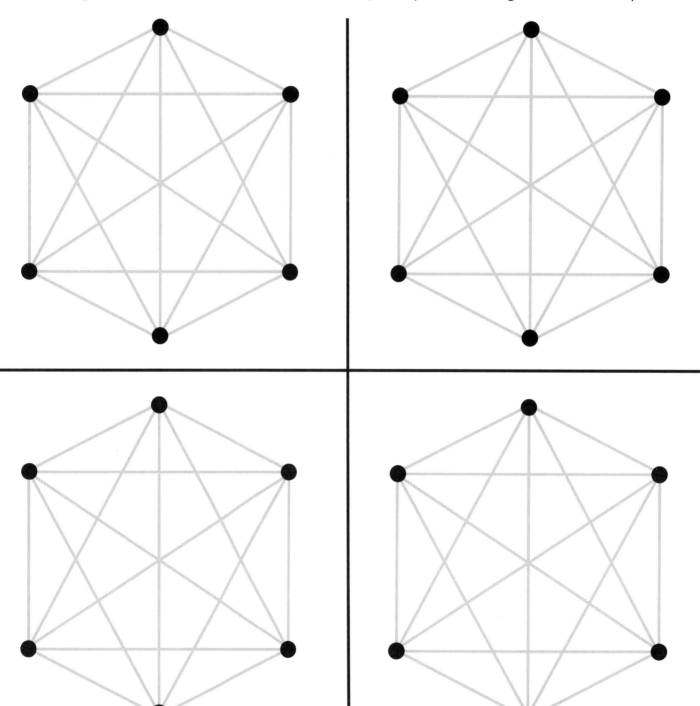

Connector

GOAL
Create the largest group of connected dots.

RULES
1. Players each have a unique color.
2. Players take turns. On a turn put a dot of your color in any open box, then eliminate any neighboring box by completely filling it in. Boxes can be eliminated in any direction, including diagonally.
3. Play until no more moves are possible.
4. The winner is the player who can create the largest group of connected dots in their color. Connections in any direction, including diagonal, count.

Example of end game. Black wins 6 to 5.

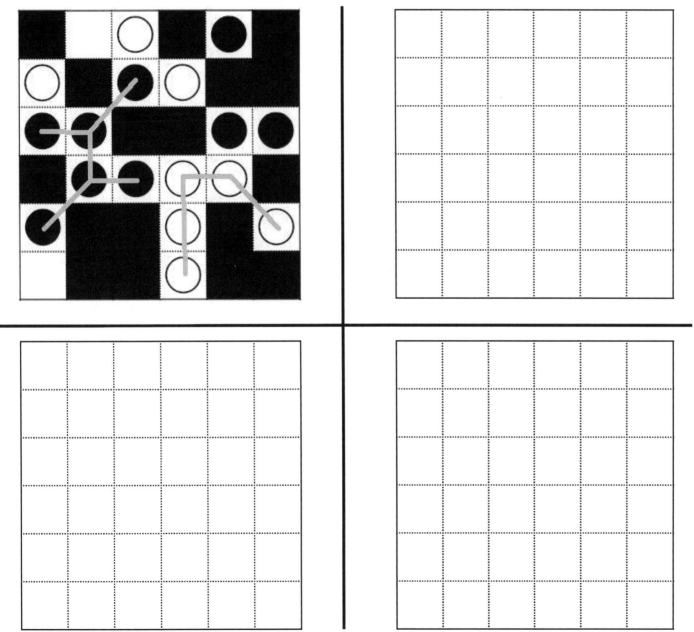

Aggression

GOAL

Control the most territories at game end.

RULES

The game is played in two phases: placement and attacking.

PLACEMENT PHASE

1. Each player begins with 40 armies.
2. Take turns choosing an empty region and placing any number of armies into that region by writing the number there.
3. When armies are placed in a region, subtract that number from the available remaining total, which you can keep track of next to the map below.
4. If a player has no armies left or there are no empty regions remaining, they must pass.
5. This phase continues until both players have passed.

ATTACKING PHASE

1. The player who passed first in the placement phase goes first.
2. Take turns selecting an opponent region and counting the number of attacking armies in all adjacent regions. If the combined strength of the attacking army is greater than the defending region, then the attacker wins. Cross out the defeated army. The attacking player loses nothing.
3. Continue until no more attacks are possible. The winner is the player with the most regions. In case of a tie, higher total army strength wins.

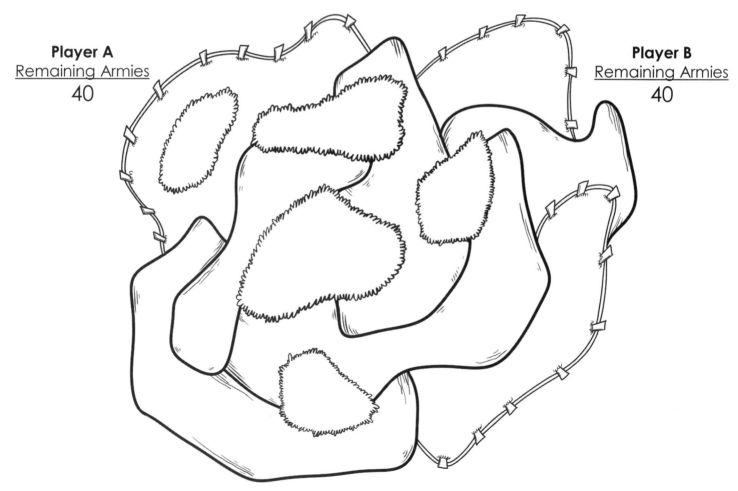

Player A
Remaining Armies
40

Player B
Remaining Armies
40

Answers

Congratulations! You made it. You've finished the book.
Did you get the right answers? Come have a look.
Were you correct? Can you answer "yes"?
If so, well done on amazing success.

Did you make a mistake? No need for concern.
Sometimes we mess up. It's a great chance to learn.
I don't have to tell you. You already know.
Every mistake is a great chance to grow.

Which shadow is correct?

4

Circle the same two pictures.

5

Connect the missing halves.

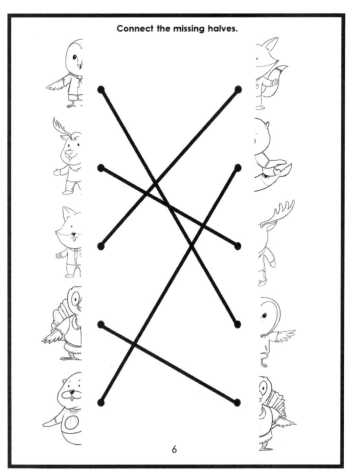

6

Can you copy it?

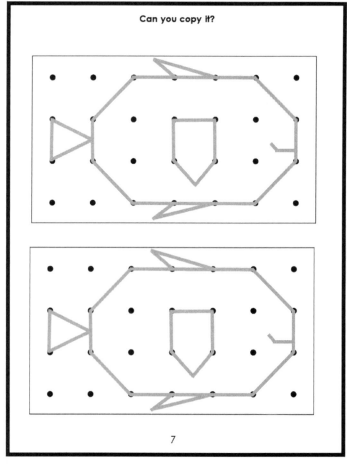

7

88

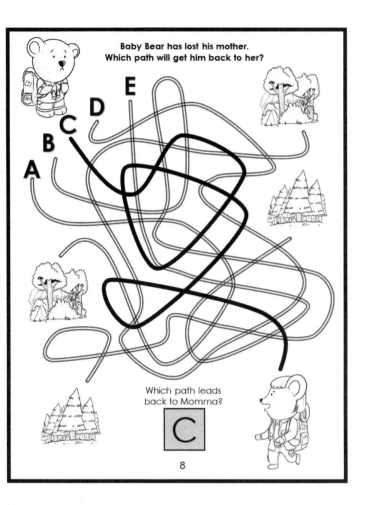

Baby Bear has lost his mother. Which path will get him back to her?

E
D
C
B
A

Which path leads back to Momma?

C

8

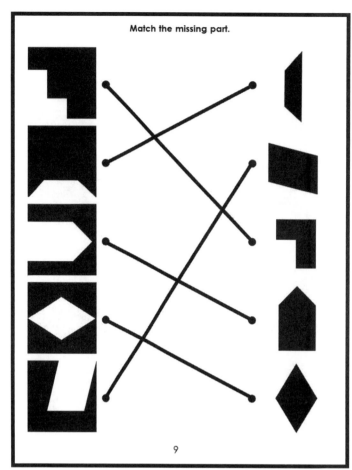

Match the missing part.

9

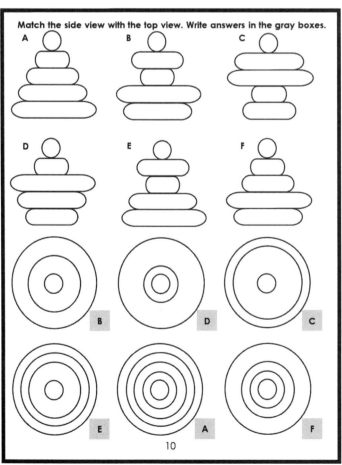

Match the side view with the top view. Write answers in the gray boxes.

A   B   C

D   E   F

B   D   C

E   A   F

10

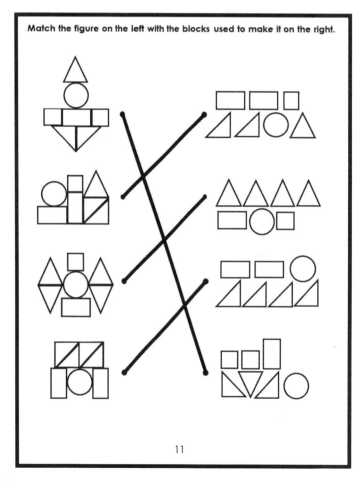

Match the figure on the left with the blocks used to make it on the right.

11

89

Each of these knots is different.
Count the number of ropes in each knot.

12

How many hay bales are there?

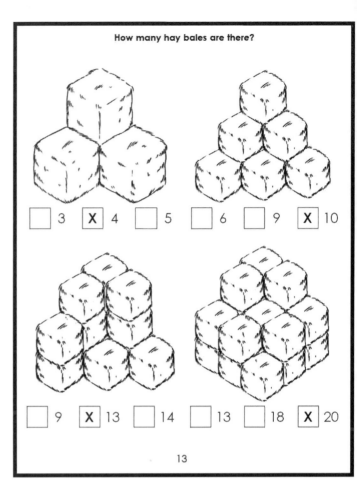

☐ 3 ☒ 4 ☐ 5   ☐ 6 ☐ 9 ☒ 10

☐ 9 ☒ 13 ☐ 14   ☐ 13 ☐ 18 ☒ 20

13

Which way will the gray gear spin? Circle the correct answer.

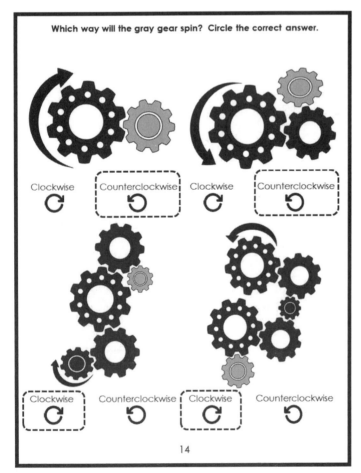

14

What shape in group 2 is the same shape as group 1?

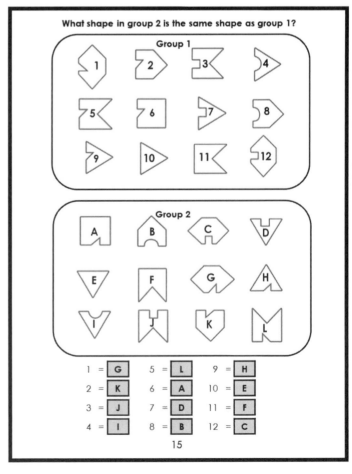

1 = G   5 = L   9 = H
2 = K   6 = A   10 = E
3 = J   7 = D   11 = F
4 = I   8 = B   12 = C

15

Fun with lines!

Can you figure out how to connect all nine dots with four straight lines without lifting your pencil or retracing?

Connect the matching numbers without crossing lines and staying inside the box.

A farmer has 15 pigs to feed. He starts in the lower right-hand stall represented by the circle. Can you draw a path that allows him to visit each pig only once and exit through stall 1?

Begin wherever you want and draw one line through all the doors, but you cannot go through the same door twice.

Begin and end at the black star. Trace a path to make a continuous line that passes through all the dots without retracing.

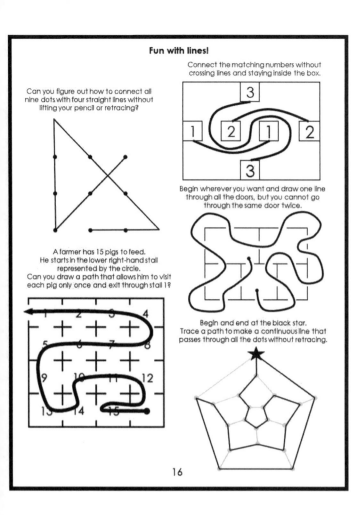

16

Lambie is on his way to school. Can you trace the shortest path?

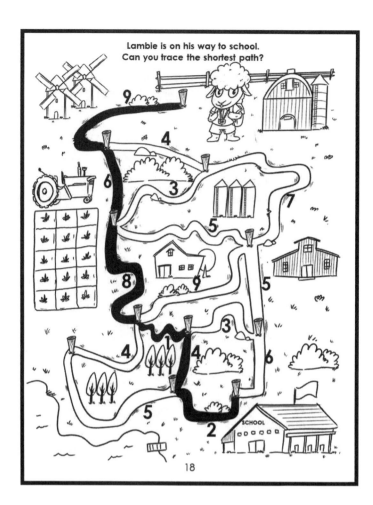

18

Figure out the value of each shape and write the answers in the boxes provided.

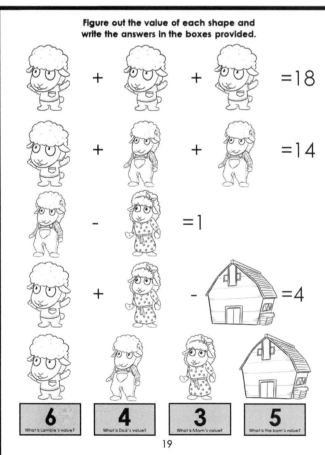

6	**4**	**3**	**5**
What is Lambie's value?	What is Dad's value?	What is Mom's value?	What is the barn's value?

19

For each puzzle, place available numbers into empty squares so that the sum is equal to the number indicated.

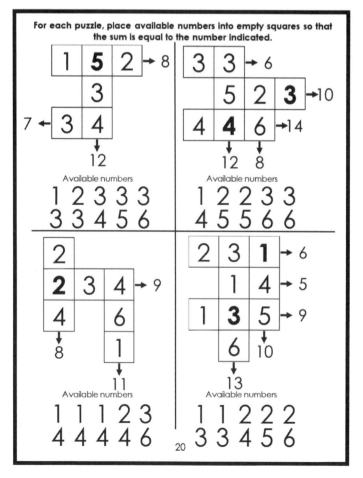

20

Puzzle 21

Fill in the gray squares with the correct number to make each equation true.

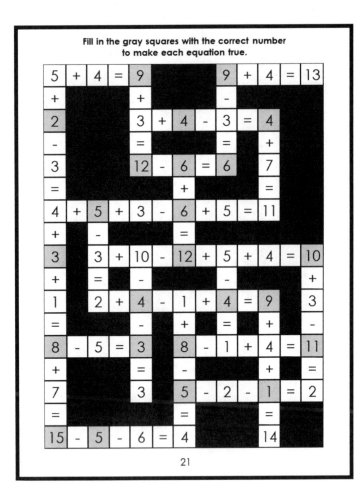

5	+	4	=	9			9	+	4	=	13
+				+					-		
2			3	+	4	-	3	=	4		
-			=				=		+		
3			12	-	6	=	6		7		
=					+				=		
4	+	5	+	3	-	6	+	5	=	11	
+		-			=						
3		3	+	10	-	12	+	5	+	4	= 10
+		=		-				-		+	
1		2	+	4	-	1	+	4	=	9	3
=			-		+		=		+		-
8	-	5	=	3		8	-	1	+	4	= 11
+			=		-			+		=	
7			3		5	-	2	-	1	=	2
=				=			=				
15	-	5	-	6	=	4			14		

Puzzle 22

Fill in the gray squares with the correct operator (+ or -) to make each equation true.

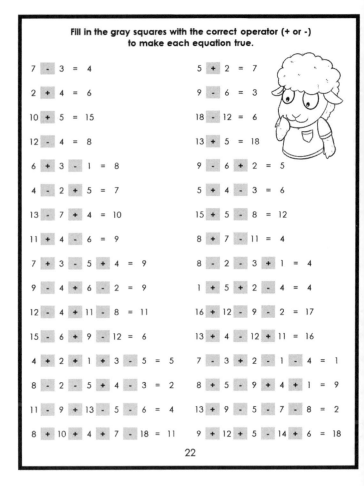

7 − 3 = 4	5 + 2 = 7
2 + 4 = 6	9 − 6 = 3
10 + 5 = 15	18 − 12 = 6
12 − 4 = 8	13 + 5 = 18
6 + 3 − 1 = 8	9 − 6 + 2 = 5
4 − 2 + 5 = 7	5 + 4 − 3 = 6
13 − 7 + 4 = 10	15 + 5 − 8 = 12
11 + 4 − 6 = 9	8 + 7 − 11 = 4
7 + 3 − 5 + 4 = 9	8 − 2 − 3 + 1 = 4
9 − 4 + 6 − 2 = 9	1 + 5 + 2 − 4 = 4
12 − 4 + 11 − 8 = 11	16 + 12 − 9 − 2 = 17
15 − 6 + 9 − 12 = 6	13 + 4 − 12 + 11 = 16
4 + 2 + 1 + 3 − 5 = 5	7 − 3 + 2 + 1 − 4 = 1
8 − 2 − 5 + 4 − 3 = 2	8 + 5 − 9 + 4 + 1 = 9
11 − 9 + 13 − 5 − 6 = 4	13 + 9 − 5 − 7 − 8 = 2
8 + 10 + 4 + 7 − 18 = 11	9 + 12 + 5 − 14 + 6 = 18

Puzzle 23

Divide each grid into rectangular or square pieces. Each piece must contain exactly one number. That number must represent the area of the rectangle. The first one is completed as an example.

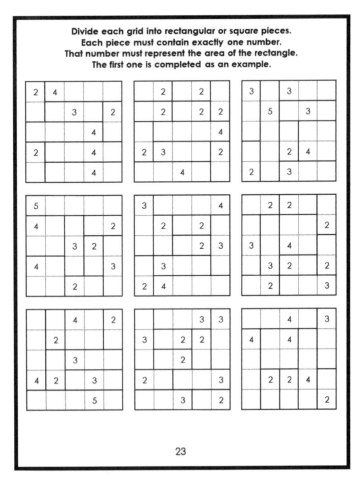

Puzzle 24

The sum of each row (↔) and column (↕) are given. What number does each animal represent?

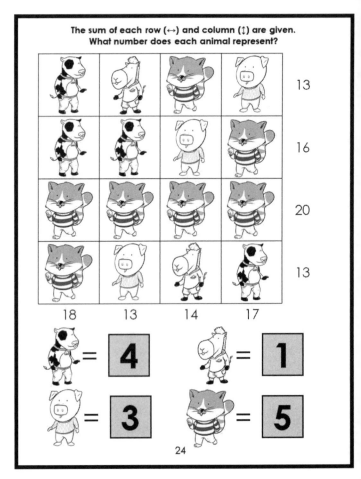

Page 25

**Each puzzle must contain all numbers 1 to 9.
Some numbers have been provided.
Fill in the gray boxes to make the equations true.**

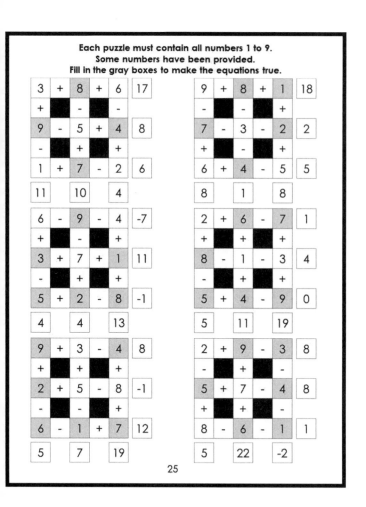

Page 26

**Study the first row (↔) and find the number pattern.
Use the same pattern to fill out the rest of the rows.**

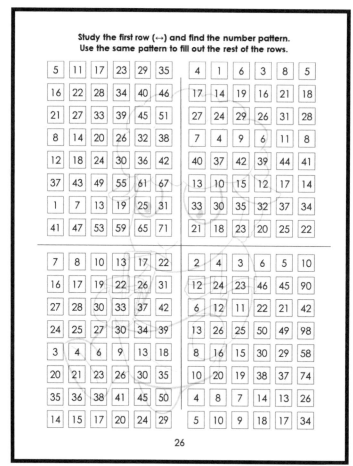

Page 27

**Within every large square, each row (↔), column (↕), and mini-grid
must contain the numbers 1, 2, 3, and 4.**

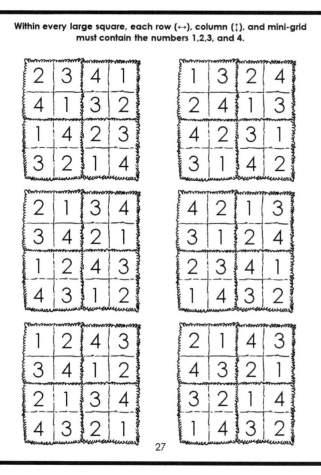

Page 28

**The mouse is hungry for cheese but can only carry three pieces!
For each puzzle, find the highest possible total value of cheese.
Start anywhere and collect three numbers by following the paths.
No jumping or going back over a path twice.**

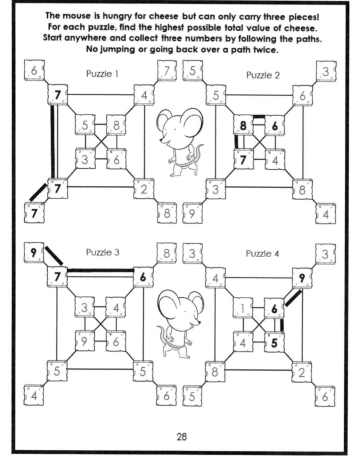

Puzzle 1   Puzzle 2   Puzzle 3   Puzzle 4

Which animal pairing will balance the teeter totter?
Circle the correct answer.

A   B   C   D

29

Determine the pattern for each shape and
write the correct answer in the gray area.

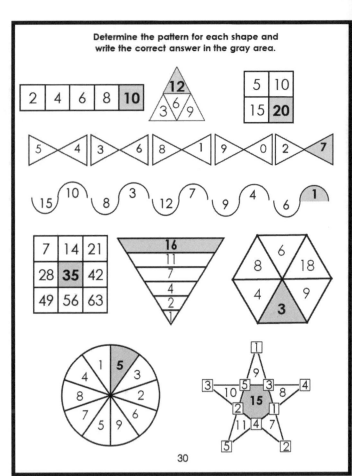

30

Circle who will win the race if everybody starts at the same time, stays
in their own lane, and goes the same speed.

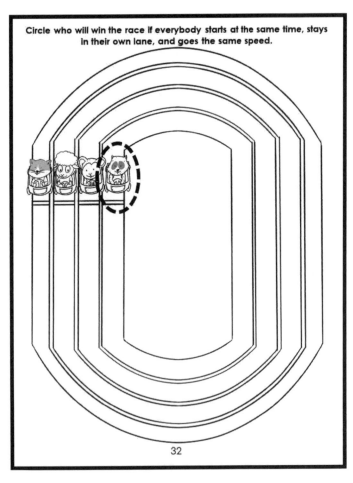

32

What is the correct picture for each relationship?

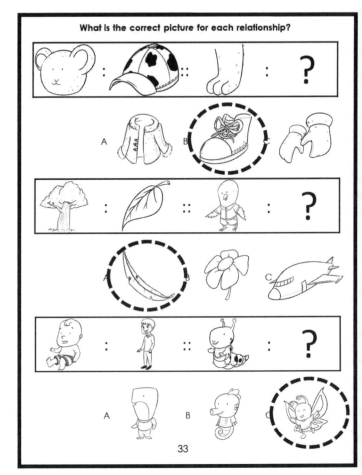

33

What date is Lambie's birthday?

- Lambie's first day of school is one week after swim lessons ended.
- Lambie's birthday is three days before his basketball game.
- Swim lessons ended 13 days ago from today.
- Lambie's trip to Grandma's is the Saturday before his first day of school.
- Today is the 25th.
- Lambie's basketball game is two weeks after his trip to Grandma's.

Can you use this calendar to help figure out Lambie's birthday?

Sunday	Monday	Tuesday	Wednesday	Thursday	Friday	Saturday
	1	2	3	4	5	6	7
8	9	10	11	12	13	14
15	16	17	18	19	20	21
22	23	24	25	26	27	28
29	30	31				

34

Where is everyone standing?

- Skunk is four spots to the left (←) of Squirrel.
- Dad is between Squirrel and Mom.
- Cow is six spaces away from Dad.
- Squirrel is two spots to the right (→) of Horse.
- Mom is five spaces to the right (→) of Lambie.
- Horse is in spot 4.
- Cat is three spaces to the left (←) of Mom.
- Lambie is in between Skunk and Horse.

Can you draw lines from each character to where they are standing?

1   2   3   4   5   6   7   8

35

Where is everyone seated at the game table?

- Horse is seated six seats clockwise (↻) from Mom.
- Lambie is two seats clockwise (↻) from Dad.
- Badger is seated two seats clockwise (↻) from Pig.
- Raccoon is seated between Lambie and Dad.
- Cow is across the table from Badger.
- Mom is seated three seats counterclockwise (↺) from Raccoon.
- Dad is seated three seats counterclockwise (↺) from Cow.

Can you draw a line from the character to where they are sitting?

36

How did everybody finish the game and what were the scores?

- Horse finished with three points more than Pig.
- Badger finished with half as many points as Dad.
- Lambie had four times as many points as Mom.
- Raccoon finished three points ahead of Cow.
- Pig finished with two points.
- Mom lost to Raccoon by nine points.
- Cow had twice as many points as Horse.
- Dad finished four points behind Lambie.

Can you fill out these squares to show what place everybody finished and what their scores were?

	Points	Place		Points	Place
(sheep)	16	1st	(raccoon)	13	2nd
(sheep)	4	7th	(cow)	10	4th
(sheep)	12	3rd	(horse)	5	6th
(badger)	6	5th	(pig)	2	8th

37

95

Put numbers in each puzzle so that no two consecutive numbers are connected by a line. For one of these, this is not possible. Can you figure out which one?

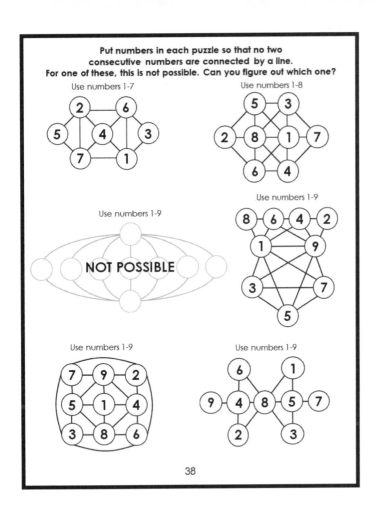

Use numbers 1-7

Use numbers 1-8

Use numbers 1-9

NOT POSSIBLE

Use numbers 1-9

Use numbers 1-9

Use numbers 1-9

38

Connect the matching shapes without overlapping any lines or shapes.

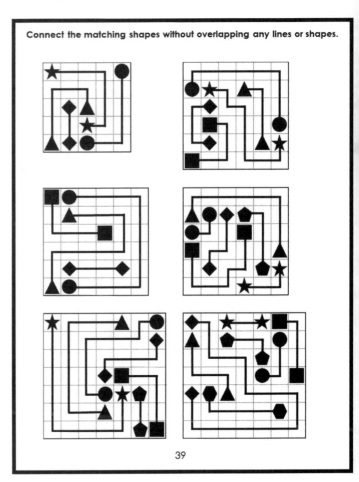

39

What is the correct path Lambie should take to get home without stepping in a puddle?

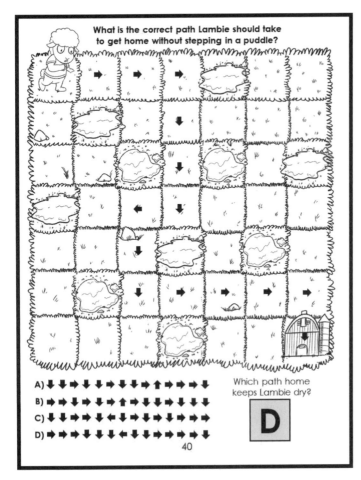

A) ↓↓➡↓➡➡➡➡⬆⬆➡➡⬆
B) ➡➡↓➡↓⬆⬆↓↓↓↓↓
C) ↓↓➡➡➡⬅⬅⬅⬅↓↓↓➡↓
D) ➡➡➡↓↓↓↓⬅↓↓➡➡➡⬇↓

Which path home keeps Lambie dry?

D

40

When Toad lands on a shape, he hops the represented three steps.

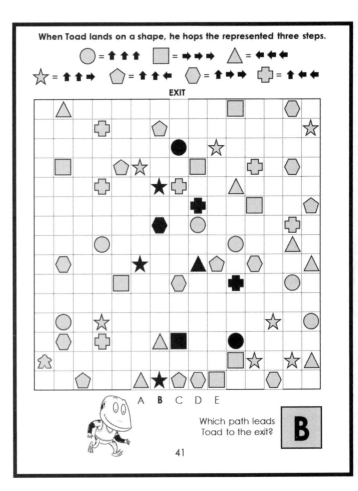

EXIT

A B C D E

Which path leads Toad to the exit?

B

41

96

It is lunchtime at school. The animals all have seating preferences.

- Kangaroo wants to share a corner with Lambie.
- Ostrich wants three seats between him and Turtle.
- Chameleon wants to sit on a side with two other animals.
- Beaver wants to be on the opposite side of the table from Lambie.
- Goat does not want to sit next to Kangaroo.
- Turtle wants to share a corner with Lambie.
- Koala wants exactly one seat between her and Ostrich.

Can you put each animal in a seat while meeting all their preferences?

42

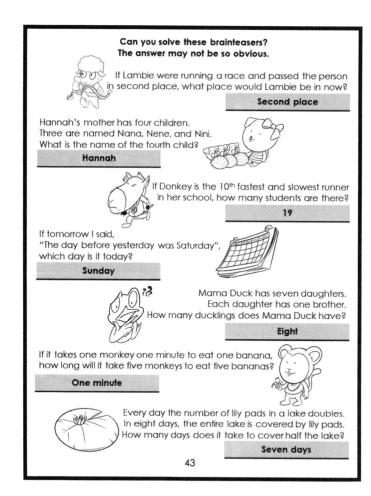

If Lambie were running a race and passed the person in second place, what place would Lambie be in now?

Second place

Hannah's mother has four children. Three are named Nana, Nene, and Nini. What is the name of the fourth child?

Hannah

If Donkey is the 10th fastest and slowest runner in her school, how many students are there?

19

If tomorrow I said, "The day before yesterday was Saturday", which day is it today?

Sunday

Mama Duck has seven daughters. Each daughter has one brother. How many ducklings does Mama Duck have?

Eight

If it takes one monkey one minute to eat one banana, how long will it take five monkeys to eat five bananas?

One minute

Every day the number of lily pads in a lake doubles. In eight days, the entire lake is covered by lily pads. How many days does it take to cover half the lake?

Seven days

43

Draw a single non-intersecting loop that passes through all circles. When you reach a circle, the line must turn. The first one is started.

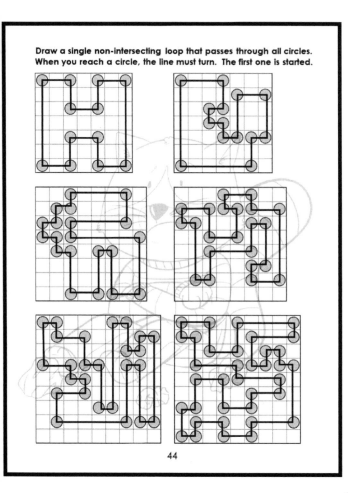

44

Circle the letter that cannot be made with the shapes on the left.

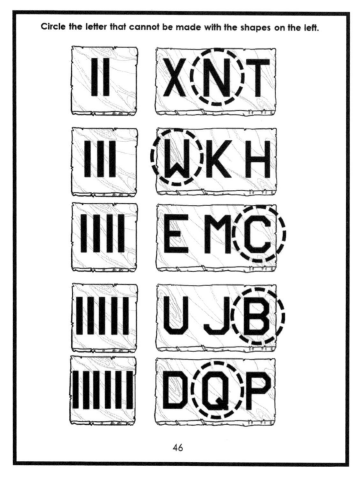

46

97

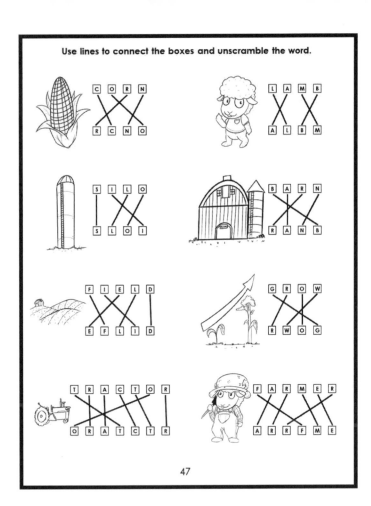

Use lines to connect the boxes and unscramble the word.

CORN — RCNO

LAMB — ALBM

SILO — SLOI

BARN — RANB

FIELD — EFLID

GROW — RWOG

TRACTOR — ORATCTR

FARMER — ARRFME

47

Cross out the extra letter in each animal's name.

R■OOSTER   BUFFA■LO   CROC■ODILE

DOLPH■IN   SP■IDER   PEA■COCK

SHAR■K   RED P■ANDA   LO■BSTER

48

Find the hidden words.
Words can go in these directions: ➡ ⬅ ⬆ ⬇ ⬊ ⬋ ⬉ ⬈

```
M R A F G F B B W G Z A F J J
V L G O I Q O A R R U X A D I
O O O L A M B I E P P B T A Q
C O W C K J T B A M C A T Q U
S H N W O T N J X D R E I I R
F A K H Y B C E A Y P W T P U
P R A C T I C E P A K D U E G
D H S N F T I T I Y R Y D E B
H G D U L B E F G V F L E H C
E O Q O U J U Y Y I Q Y S S H
Q Z R E K B R Y B D N E B T J
I W G S K A C N D T M D D M A
C D E T E R M I N A T I O N Q
M M F D P N R P G W M C O U A
W F D P E R S E V E R A N C E
```

ATTITUDE	COW	GAMES	LAMBIE	PRACTICE
BARN	DETERMINATION	GRITTY	PERSEVERANCE	SHEEP
CAT	FARM	HORSE	PIG	YET

49

Write the names of the animals in the correct space.

LEOPARD

FROG

TORTOISE

ELEPHANT

HEDGEHOG

WOLF

PENGUIN

50

98

Page 51

In the story below there are hidden animal names in some of the words. Can you find all of them?

Lambie wanted to help his **moth**er prepare dinner. This was his first time helping in the kitc**hen**.

"I want to make a mil**lion** b**rat**wursts!" exclaimed Lambie.

"Oh, honey. That's far too many for our family," replied Mommy.

"That's ok, we can s**hare** with the whole barnyard," said Lambie.

"I like your enthusiasm but let's keep it simple for your first time. I could use your help with these g**rape**s," Mommy said with smile.

Lambie had eaten them before but didn't know how to help. He had lots of questions. "How **doe**s it work? What do I do? Do I need to p**eel** them?" asked Lambie.

"No, silly," said Mommy. "I just need you to take this **bat**ch, pluck them off and put them in this b**owl**. If any fall, try to **cat**ch them before they hit the floor and if you miss, we need to throw them away, even if they have **bee**n on the ground only brief**fly**."

"I did it!" **boa**sted Lambie. "I picked my first one!"

"You did fantastic," Mommy said. "Keep going and when you are done you can put them next to the guaca**mole** and help yourself to ca**ram**el for all your hard work!"

~ANIMALS~							
ape	bat	bee	boa	cat	doe	eel	fly
hare	hen	lion	mole	~~moth~~	owl	ram	rat

51

Page 52

Use the key below to solve the three coded messages.

A B C D E F G H I J K L M N O P Q R S T U V W X Y Z
15 3 8 22 12 26 6 20 16 10 19 4 24 13 9 1 23 7 21 2 11 17 14 25 5 18

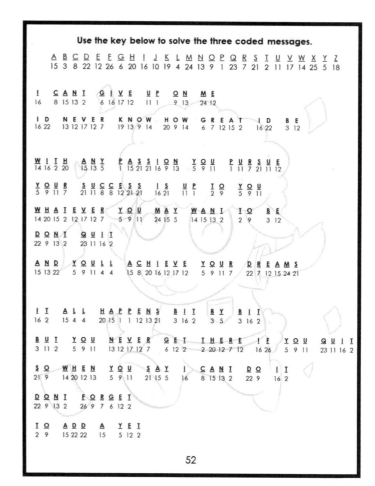

I CAN'T GIVE UP ON ME
16 8 15 13 2   6 16 17 12   11 1   9 13   24 12

I'D NEVER KNOW HOW GREAT I'D BE
16 22   13 12 17 12 7   19 13 9 14   20 9 14   6 7 12 15 2   16 22   3 12

WITH ANY PASSION YOU PURSUE
14 16 2 20   15 13 5   1 15 21 16 9 13   5 9 11   1 11 7 21 11 12

YOUR SUCCESS IS UP TO YOU
5 9 11 7   21 11 8 8 12 21 21   16 21   11 1   2 9   5 9 11

WHATEVER YOU MAY WANT TO BE
14 20 15 2 12 17 12 7   5 9 11   24 15 5   14 15 13 2   2 9   3 12

DON'T QUIT
22 9 13 2   23 11 16 2

AND YOU'LL ACHIEVE YOUR DREAMS
15 13 22   5 9 11 4 4   15 8 20 16 12 17 12   5 9 11 7   22 7 12 15 24 21

IT ALL HAPPENS BIT BY BIT
16 2   15 4 4   20 15 1 1 12 13 21   3 16 2   3 5   3 16 2

BUT YOU NEVER GET THERE IF YOU QUIT
3 11 2   5 9 11   13 12 17 12 7   6 12 2   2 20 12 7 12   16 26   5 9 11   23 11 16 2

SO WHEN YOU SAY I CAN'T DO IT
21 9   14 20 12 13   5 9 11   21 15 5   16   8 15 13 2   22 9   16 2

DON'T FORGET
22 9 13 2   26 9 7 6 12 2

TO ADD A YET
2 9   15 22 22   15   5 12 2

52

Page 53

Each of these foods has a double letter in the name. Can you fill in the blanks?

P E P P E R S

A P P L E

C O O K I E

M U F F I N

C A R R O T

B E R R I E S

W A F F L E

B U T T E R

C A B B A G E

S P A G H E T T I

P I Z Z A

B R O C C O L I

C H E E S E

E G G S

L E T T U C E

P I N E A P P L E

C H E R R Y

J E L L Y

53

Page 54

Unscramble the words to discover the animal names. The first one is done for you.

❶ DICE COLOR
CROCODILE

❷ NO RICH ROSE
RHINOCEROS

❸ JAB AT BRICK
JACK RABBIT

❹ SCOOT UP
OCTOPUS

❺ FIG FEAR
GIRAFFE

❻ PATIO PUSH MOP
HIPPOPOTAMUS

❼ NEAT HELP
ELEPHANT

❽ IN A MOON UNTIL
MOUNTAIN LION

❾ RADIO GRIPE
PRAIRIE DOG

❿ DECENT PIE
CENTIPEDE

~ANIMALS~
GIRAFFE
HIPPOPOTAMUS
RHINOCEROS
JACK RABBIT
PRAIRIE DOG
~~CROCODILE~~
CENTIPEDE
OCTOPUS
MOUNTAIN LION
ELEPHANT

54

Page 55

To make a word, take a letter or combination of letters from each barn.
Make four words for each group of barns.
The first word in each group has been done for you.

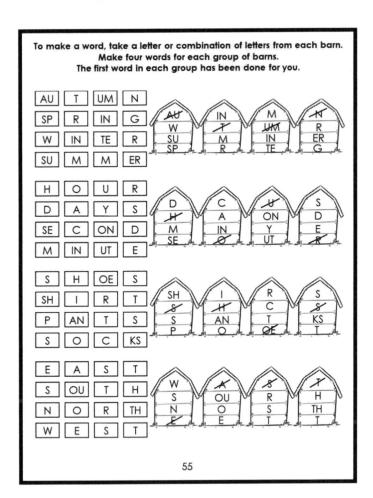

AU	T	UM	N
SP	R	IN	G
W	IN	TE	R
SU	M	M	ER

Barns: AU / W / SU / SP — IN / T / M / R — M / UM / IN / TE — N / ER / G

H	O	U	R
D	A	Y	S
SE	C	ON	D
M	IN	UT	E

Barns: D / M / SE — C / A / IN / O — U / ON / Y / UT — S / D / E

S	H	OE	S
SH	I	R	T
P	AN	T	S
S	O	C	KS

Barns: SH / S / S / P — I / H / AN / O — R / C / T / OE — S / S / KS / T

E	A	S	T
S	OU	T	H
N	O	R	TH
W	E	S	T

Barns: W / S / N — A / OU / O / E — S / R / S — T / H / TH

Page 56

Using the letters available, can you write down
at least five words of any length for each puzzle?
Use each letter at most only one time per word.

Wheel 1: A E S T R

ARE	EAST	RATES	SET
ART	EAT	REAST	STAR
ARTS	EATS	REST	STARE
AT	ERA	SAT	TAR
ATE	ERAS	SEA	TEA
EAR	RAT	SEAR	TEAR
EARS	RATE	SEAT	TEARS

Wheel 2: D G A O T

AD	GOAT	TO
AT	GOD	TOAD
DO	GOT	
DOG	OAT	
DOT	TAD	
GO	TAG	

Page 57

Follow the instructions to crack the coded message.

Coded message:

LITTL ELAMB IELOV EDTOP LAYIF HEHAD HISWA YHEDP LAYAL LDAYB
UILDI NGTOW ERSPL AYGRO UNDSL IDESJ UMPIN GHANG INGWA
GONRI DESBL OWING BUBBL ESCLI MBING TREES NEARL YALLA CTIVI
TIESW HENAS KEDHI SFAVO RITEH EEXCL AIMST HERES NOTHI NGILO
VEMOR ETHAN GAMES

Decoded message:

Print out the complete coded message in capital letters, with no spaces
between letters. Mark a slash (/) between words as they appear to you.

....

....

....

....

....

....

Cleartext message:

Write out the complete message in plain English.

Little Lambie loved to play.
If he had his way, he'd play all day.
Building towers. Playground slides.
Jumping. Hanging. Wagon rides.
Blowing bubbles. Climbing trees.
Nearly all activities.
When asked his favorite he exclaims,
"There's nothing I love more than games!"

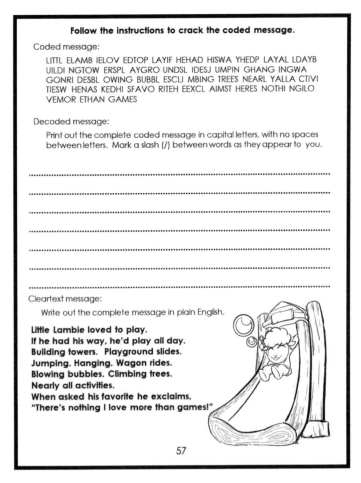

Page 58

Can you figure out the phrase for each of these word puzzles?
Consider how the words are written, the number of times,
their direction, and placement.

1 R ROAD A D	2 CHAIR	3 MAN / BOARD
4 FOUR (FOUR vertical both sides) FOUR	5 CYCLE CYCLE CYCLE	6 HEAT
7 MERRY GO (circular)	8 READ (between lines)	9 S S I I D D E E

1 Crossroads	2 Highchair	3 Man overboard
4 Four square	5 Tricycle	6 Heat wave
7 Merry-go-round	8 Read between the lines	9 Side by side

What was last month and what is next month?

LAST MONTH	THIS MONTH	NEXT MONTH
APRIL	MAY	JUNE
AUGUST	SEPTEMBER	OCTOBER
JANUARY	FEBRUARY	MARCH
JUNE	JULY	AUGUST
MARCH	APRIL	MAY
SEPTEMBER	OCTOBER	NOVEMBER
NOVEMBER	DECEMBER	JANUARY
DECEMBER	JANUARY	FEBRUARY
MAY	JUNE	JULY
OCTOBER	NOVEMBER	DECEMBER
FEBRUARY	MARCH	APRIL
JULY	AUGUST	SEPTEMBER

60

What day was yesterday and what day is tomorrow?

YESTERDAY	TODAY	TOMORROW
THURSDAY	FRIDAY	SATURDAY
TUESDAY	WEDNESDAY	THURSDAY
SATURDAY	SUNDAY	MONDAY
WEDNESDAY	THURSDAY	FRIDAY
FRIDAY	SATURDAY	SUNDAY
MONDAY	TUESDAY	WEDNESDAY
SUNDAY	MONDAY	TUESDAY

How many?

60	Seconds in a minute
60	Minutes in an hour
24	Hours in a day
7	Days in a week
52	Weeks in a year

61

Connect the dots!

62

Help Lambie get to his ball!

63

101

Hidden pictures!

Can you find?

Can you find and circle 16 differences between these pictures?

65

Count the objects hidden in the drawing.

3 **3** **9** **5** **4**

66

How many of each shape are there?

☐ = **5**   ⬡ = **5**   ⬠ = **6**

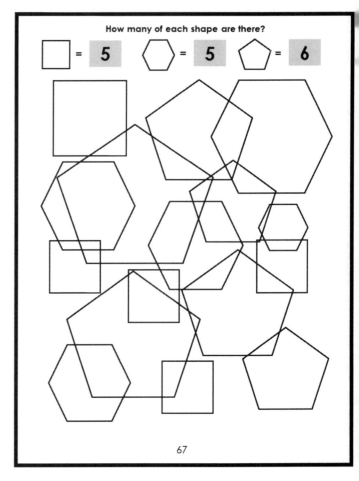

67

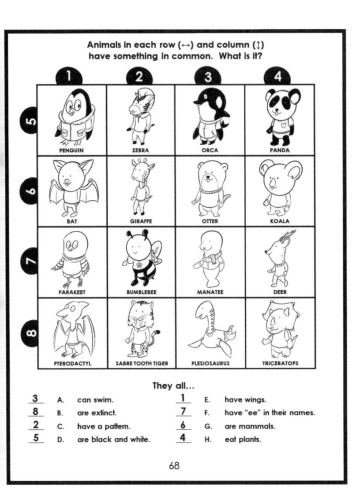

Animals in each row (↔) and column (↕) have something in common. What is it?

	1	**2**	**3**	**4**
5	PENGUIN	ZEBRA	ORCA	PANDA
6	BAT	GIRAFFE	OTTER	KOALA
7	PARAKEET	BUMBLEBEE	MANATEE	DEER
8	PTERODACTYL	SABRE TOOTH TIGER	PLESIOSAURUS	TRICERATOPS

They all...

_3_ A. can swim.

_8_ B. are extinct.

_2_ C. have a pattern.

_5_ D. are black and white.

_1_ E. have wings.

_7_ F. have "ee" in their names.

_6_ G. are mammals.

_4_ H. eat plants.

68

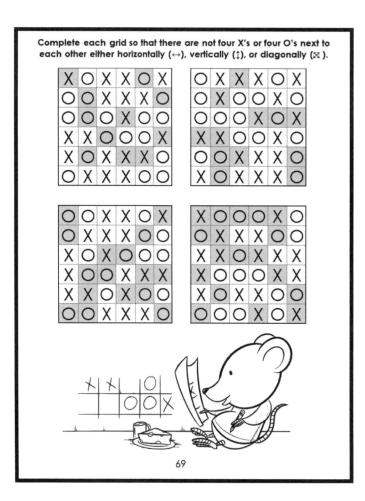

Complete each grid so that there are not four X's or four O's next to each other either horizontally (↔), vertically (↕), or diagonally (⊠).

69

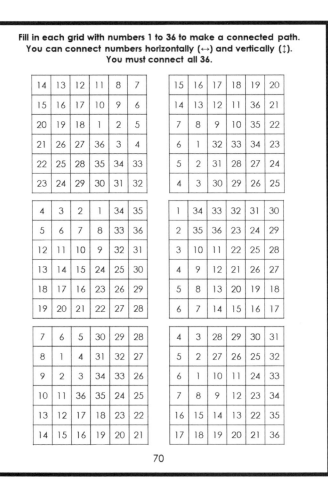

Fill in each grid with numbers 1 to 36 to make a connected path. You can connect numbers horizontally (↔) and vertically (↕). You must connect all 36.

70

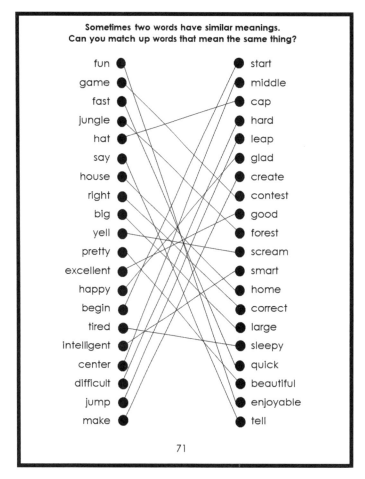

Sometimes two words have similar meanings. Can you match up words that mean the same thing?

fun · · start
game · · middle
fast · · cap
jungle · · hard
hat · · leap
say · · glad
house · · create
right · · contest
big · · good
yell · · forest
pretty · · scream
excellent · · smart
happy · · home
begin · · correct
tired · · large
intelligent · · sleepy
center · · quick
difficult · · beautiful
jump · · enjoyable
make · · tell

71

103

Certificate of
ACHIEVEMENT

Awarded to

_____

For their perseverance, determination and positive attitude in the face of increasingly challenging puzzles, games, and problems while completing the Logic Workbook for Gritty Kids.

This _____ *day of* _____ *in the year of* _____

Signed _____

LOGIC WORKBOOK FOR

GRITTY KIDS

THE GRITTY KIDS SERIES

Fostering grit, growth, and perseverance in children through games and stories.

for ages 3-8

for ages 6-10

for ages 8-12

HIDDEN MEEPLE ANSWER!

page 41

To Amy,
For all your love.
For all your support.
For all your patience.
For all your great ideas.
For all your understanding.
For all your encouragement.
For all the times you put up with me.
Thank you.
-DA

To Him, to my family and friends, and to all those who supported me,
may this be another fruitful second milestone for all the dreams that are yet to happen.
-AY

The following pages are intentionally blank to allow
space to further explore puzzles or play additional games.

Text © 2021 by Dan Allbaugh
Illustrations © 2021 by Anil Yap
ISBN: 978-1-7357708-3-3

Green Meeple Books

greenmeeplebooks.com